0 5
▼

MAY 16, 2016

"DRAGONS" IS RELEASED.

May 22, 2016

"HERO" IS RELEASED.

MAY 24, 2016

OVERWATCH IS LAUNCHED,
ACCOMPANIED BY THE "ARE YOU WITH US?"
ANIMATED SHORT.

0 6
▼

0 7
▼

JULY 12, 2016

THE ANA ORIGIN STORY IS RELEASED.

NOVEMBER 4, 2016

"INFILTRATION" AND THE SOMBRA ORIGIN
STORY ARE REVEALED AT BLIZZCON.

AUGUST 18, 2016

"THE LAST BASTION" IS RELEASED.

THE CINEMATIC ART OF

OVERWATCH

VOLUME I
2014–2016

TITAN BOOKS

BLIZZARD
ENTERTAINMENT

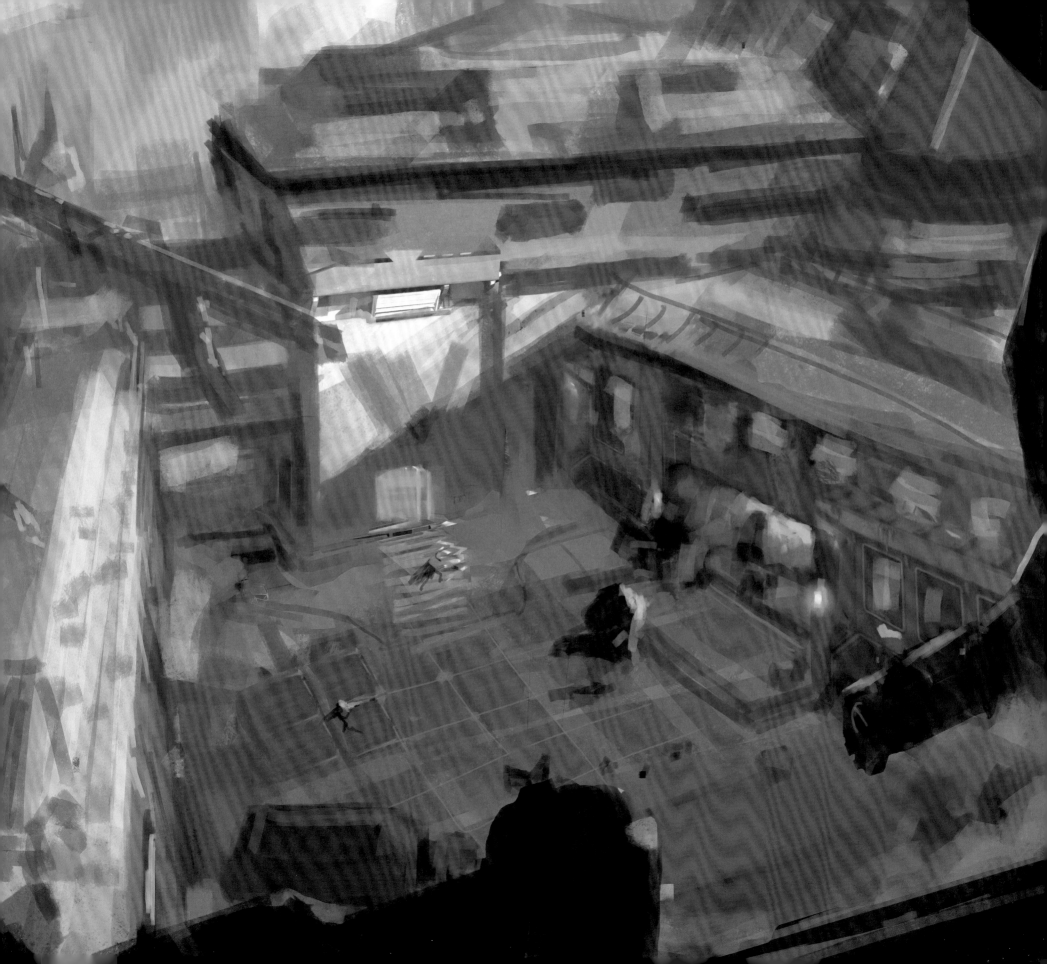

INTRODUCTION

ONE ▼

"IT HAS BEEN SOMETHING LIKE SEVENTEEN YEARS SINCE BLIZZARD OPENED THE DOOR TO A NEW ADVENTURE, SINCE WE OPENED THE DOOR TO A NEW WORLD OF heroes and villains," creative director Chris Metzen said to the packed audience at BlizzCon's opening ceremony on November 7, 2014.

Thousands of people had gathered at the Anaheim Convention Center in California, and thousands more were watching via live stream. The opening ceremony was almost over, and no one could have guessed what Metzen was about to reveal.

At the time, Blizzard was a company of long-standing franchises. Warcraft, StarCraft, and Diablo had all started in the 1990s and were still going strong with sequels and expansions. Blizzard had more recently started other franchises like Hearthstone and Heroes of the Storm, but they shared many of the same themes and characters as their predecessors. What the company hadn't done since the nineties was reveal a completely new franchise—a universe with characters different from anything it had released before.

LEFT Illustration of Tracer, Winston, and other Overwatch heroes from the announcement trailer.

"I want you to open your hearts and your minds to what comes next," Metzen said. "You are about to get a glimpse into the future. So, my friends, get a load of this. I hope you love it like we do. I'll see you on the other side."

The lights dimmed. A hush fell over the crowd. All eyes turned to the convention center's giant monitors, where a cinematic gave the world its first glimpse of Overwatch.

There were no zerg, night elves, or demons. No magi hurling spells in enchanted forests or armored marines marching through the dark corridors of a battle cruiser.

The film was set in a sleek, ultramodern museum on future Earth. Its ample light and warm colors established Overwatch's vision of a bright and optimistic future. Tracer, Winston, Reaper, and Widowmaker—four of the game's iconic heroes and villains—leaped from the screen, animated in a playful and exaggerated style that made them seem capable of anything. Their distinct personalities were accentuated by equally distinct wardrobes, from the bubbly optimist Tracer in her vivid orange jumpsuit to the brooding villain Reaper in his skull mask and black cloak. The story told by the film was about inspiring others to be heroes—a theme that was central to the Overwatch universe.

RIGHT & OPPOSITE, BOTTOM Early storyboards from the announcement trailer.

OPPOSITE, TOP Concept art of the museum from the announcement trailer.

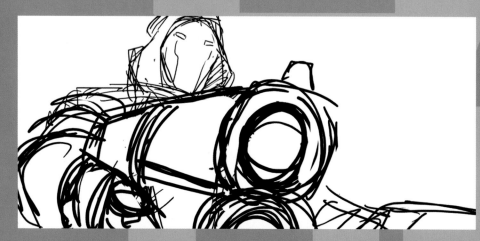

ABOVE Storyboards for the announcement trailer.

LEFT & OPPOSITE, TOP Explorations of lighting and color for the announcement trailer.

OPPOSITE, BOTTOM Concepts of the kids featured in the announcement trailer.

CHEERS, LOVE!

In under six minutes, the cinematic showed viewers the essence of Overwatch. From the thunderous applause that filled the convention center after the film ended, it was clear it had worked. The audience had embraced Overwatch's vision of the future.

But to reach that point—for Blizzard to discover what this brave new world was and *how* it could be brought to life through cinematics—had been a journey into uncharted territory.

The first step on that journey had been taken during a meeting over a year prior to *Overwatch*'s BlizzCon debut in summer 2013. *Overwatch* was still early in development, but discussions about the role cinematics would play in the new game had already started. At the meeting were Chris Metzen, *Overwatch*'s creative director; Jeff Kaplan, *Overwatch*'s game director; Ray Gresko, *Overwatch*'s executive producer; and Jeff Chamberlain, one of the directors and supervisors for Blizzard's cinematics. At that point, all options were on the table. Would the cinematics simply be one-minute commercials for the heroes? Would they be funny or serious? Would the game even need cinematics *at all*?

"I remember suggesting doing something different at that moment," said Kaplan. "The game was PvP only—an FPS action game with twelve players on the battlefield at the same time. I'm thinking, 'There's no way we can convey story in any meaningful way in the type of game we're making.'"

RIGHT In-progress illustration for the announcement trailer.

Taking that structural separation of gameplay and narrative to heart, what Kaplan suggested was simply to focus the cinematics on telling great Overwatch stories above all else. Without an in-game campaign, they could become the primary vehicle for exploring the characters, world, and backstory in-depth.

This idea of making cinematic storytelling a core feature of the Overwatch universe evolved into a larger plan. Looking beyond the announcement trailer, the team would make a series of shorts—some to drive excitement for the game leading up to its release on May 24, 2016, and others that would come out after the initial launch. Each cinematic would present new challenges and raise different questions about storytelling and art. The creators would take risks, find new ways of collaborating, and reimagine the type of art they could make at Blizzard.

There is a saying at the company that it "takes a Blizzard to make a Blizzard game." The same can be said of the cinematics. Creating films for Overwatch required dozens of talented individuals across the company to take a journey into the unknown together, empowering each other with their knowledge and passion as they worked toward a common goal. This book explores their search for the visual and thematic heart of Overwatch's cinematics and the art they created to find it.

As Metzen said at the opening ceremony, "I hope you love it like we do."

LEFT In-progress illustration for the announcement trailer.

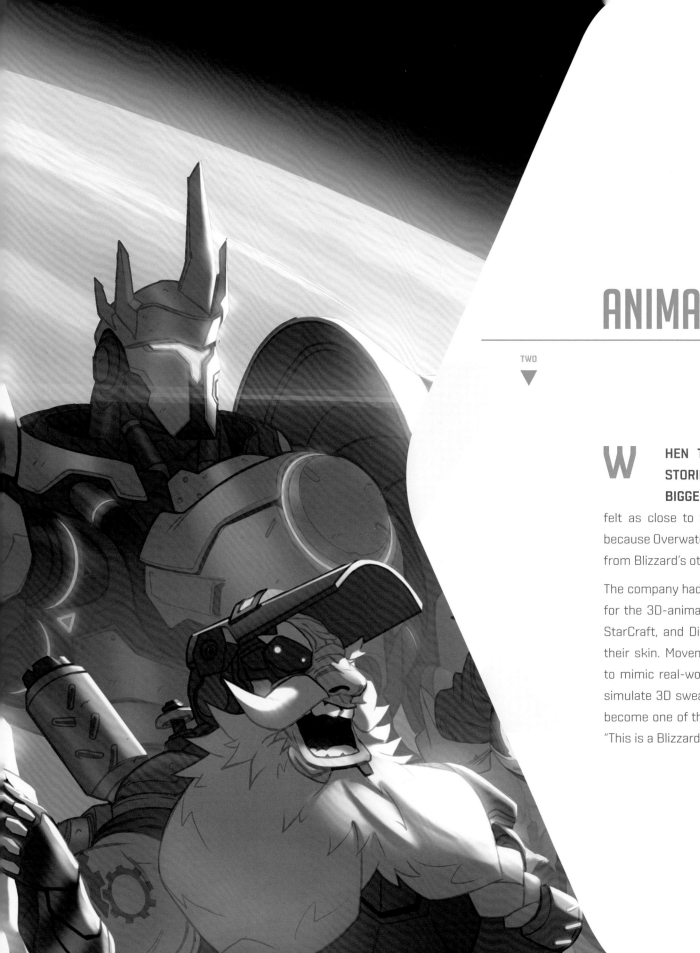

ANIMATED SHORTS

TWO
▼

WHEN THE CINEMATICS TEAM EMBARKED ON TELLING STORIES IN OVERWATCH'S NEW UNIVERSE, ONE OF THEIR BIGGEST GOALS WAS CREATING FILMS THAT LOOKED AND felt as close to the game as possible. That presented a challenge because Overwatch explores visuals and themes that are very different from Blizzard's other cinematics.

The company had spent years developing a style called "hyperrealism" for the 3D-animated cutscenes and trailers it produces for Warcraft, StarCraft, and Diablo. Characters feature thousands of tiny hairs on their skin. Movements rely on complex systems of rigging designed to mimic real-world physiology. In some cases, the filmmakers even simulate 3D sweat on a character's skin. This intensely real style had become one of the visual signatures that immediately told audiences, "This is a Blizzard cinematic."

LEFT Illustration of the Overwatch heroes for the announcement trailer.

Overwatch required a different approach. The game was designed to honor Blizzard's decades-long visual legacy, but it also has its own distinct art pillars, which give it an identity all its own. These core principles are: creating diverse characters and environments; making Overwatch's vision of the future hopeful through inspirational design, color, and lighting choices; finding a dynamic style for everything from animations to character silhouettes; and giving the game a handcrafted feel to show that it has been lovingly built by real people.

"It has more of a graphic yet painterly quality," said David Satchwell, one of the digital effects supervisors for cinematics. "When you get into a painterly animated world, I think there's a lot more flexibility for creativity in that you're not bound by the expectation of reality and what the human eye is used to seeing. It's like this is someone's vision of reality—it's not your own—so you can diverge from the norm freely."

In adopting Overwatch's art pillars for the cinematics, the team had to change their approach to how they normally made films. Hyperrealism was no longer the goal. Instead of animating the smallest details of a character's movements, they created dynamic choreography, where characters performed impossible physical feats. Rather than simulating realistic hair or effects, they handcrafted these elements whenever possible.

"It was a big artistic challenge for us. The work we were used to doing with Warcraft, StarCraft, and Diablo relied a lot on sensory overload, an avalanche of complex, exquisitely crafted details," said Mathias Verhasselt, who was the art director on many of the *Overwatch* animated shorts. "But the Overwatch style is much more minimalistic, and simple statements can often be harder to make than complicated ones."

RIGHT In-progress illustration for the "Are You With Us?" animated short.

FOLLOWING PAGES Paint-over image exploring lighting and color for the announcement trailer.

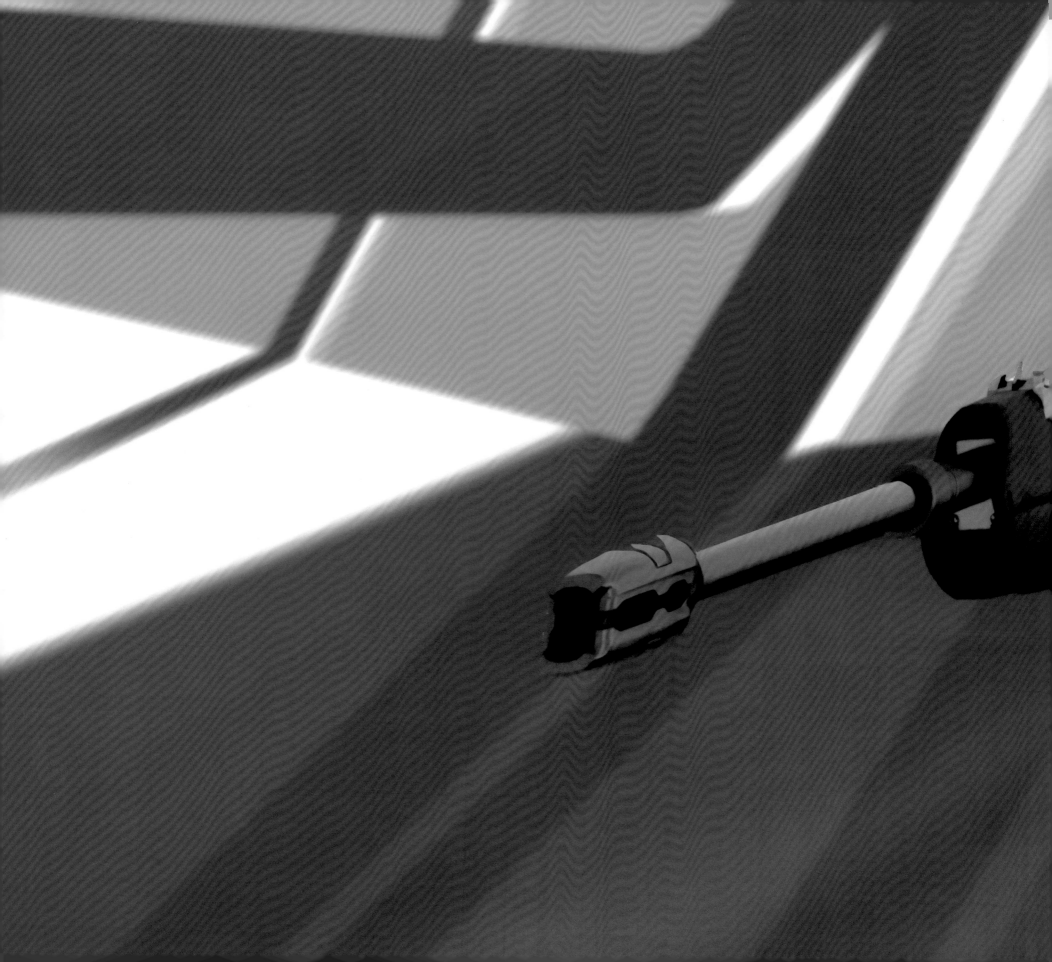

ANNOUNCEMENT TRAILER

"YOU KNOW, THE WORLD COULD
ALWAYS USE MORE HEROES."

—TRACER

RIGHT Early museum concept art.

HOW DO YOU ANNOUNCE A COMPLETELY NEW FRANCHISE TO THE WORLD?

That was the question the team wrestled with when contemplating the *Overwatch* announcement trailer, which would provide the world with its first glimpse of the new Blizzard universe. Whatever form the trailer took, it would need to accomplish many things: showcase Overwatch's unique art style, touch on its inspirational themes and futuristic setting, make people fall in love with a universe they'd never seen before, and most important, leave them wanting more.

Production began with brainstorming sessions to determine what the trailer would be about. These meetings were the beginnings of a "story room" made up of artists, producers, writers, directors, and designers, who worked on the cinematics and the game. They came together not just to make films but to discuss important questions about the game's characters and themes that would ultimately shape the world of Overwatch.

One of the biggest early discussions centered around tone. What types of stories should the cinematics tell about Overwatch, and how should they make audiences feel?

"The one thing that kept popping up in our conversations was heart," said senior storyboard artist Ted Boonthanakit, one of the trailer's storyboard artists. "We wanted to give this cinematic heart."

Then two ideas came up that changed everything. In one of the story room's brainstorming sessions, Arnold Tsang, *Overwatch*'s lead character artist at the time, suggested focusing the trailer around kids on a field trip.

No one in the meeting knew quite what to think. Kids on a field trip was very different from anything Blizzard had done before. But it didn't take long for everyone to rally around the idea. Focusing on children would allow them to unlock a bit of that elusive heart that everyone had been searching for. They could tell a story that wasn't just about heroes; it could be a statement about what heroes mean to *regular* people. "You saw these heroes through a child's eye, and the wonder that these two kids have," said senior producer Phillip Hillenbrand.

The second idea was staging the trailer in a museum. It was the perfect setting for a field trip, and it gave the team an organic way to reveal Overwatch's rich backstory. The museum and everything in it would offer hints about the new universe, its history, and the heroes who inhabit it.

THESE PAGES Early explorations of the museum environment.

Based on these ideas, Boonthanakit and senior storyboard artist Mike Koizumi were encouraged to sketch out various moments and locations for the piece and follow their inspiration. The only guidelines they had were that the story had to be about a group of heroes that had run afoul of the powers that be and were now in hiding.

Director Jeff Chamberlain worked with Boonthanakit and Koizumi to create a set of twelve beat boards—still images that conveyed the trailer's key moments. "We stripped it down to the bare bones," said Chamberlain. "It was two kids, brothers, who happened to be in this Overwatch museum when a fight breaks out."

When Chamberlain later showed the beat boards to the story room, his presentation was initially met with silence. Crestfallen, he assumed that no one liked the idea, but that wasn't the case. The members of the story room were only trying to process what they had just seen.

"There wasn't much to say other than to come out of your stunned silence with a brief staccato 'Yeah. Just make it. This is it. This is what we were talking about,'" said game director Jeff Kaplan. "It just felt right. Everyone in the room felt that way, felt very strongly about the piece."

The number of boards would grow over the course of production as storyboard artists fleshed out the trailer's other shots, but those first twelve images marked an important milestone. They turned the early brainstorming ideas into something tangible that proved the story could work.

"There was really a sense of adventure and doing something that was off the beaten path for us," said art director Stephan Belin. "Everyone was enthusiastic. When you look at the actual story of the trailer, interestingly, its hopeful themes transcribe into how we worked on the piece."

THESE PAGES Early storyboards featuring the main beats of the announcement trailer.

DEVELOPING AN AESTHETIC TOGETHER

When work began on the announcement trailer, there were many things about Overwatch's aesthetic that had yet to be determined. "Around that time, we were still developing the art style for the game," said Tsang. "Not only our art style but our process, our pillars for how we operate."

Work on the trailer began in January 2014, and the entire project had to be wrapped by BlizzCon in November of that same year. Because time was short, production of the trailer and the game ran in parallel. Making an announcement that would be true to Overwatch's visual aesthetic and meet the deadline hinged on close collaboration between everyone involved in making the cinematic and the game.

"The relationships from the beginning were very strong," said Bill Petras, *Overwatch*'s art director. "We pushed each other to be more creative and find the right vision."

Art and ideas flowed freely as the team made decisions on everything from animation style to texturing, even down to how shiny Tracer's leather jacket should be. There were few hard and fast rules. Nothing was set in stone.

ABOVE Sketch exploring statue poses.

LEFT Line art for an illustration.

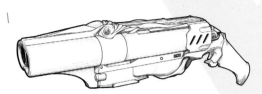

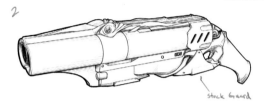

For the announcement trailer, the team initially wanted to pursue elements like realistic skin and hair, but that didn't fit Overwatch. Tracer's hair, for example, never went flat. It might move a little as she leaps around and fires her pulse pistols, but it always keeps its stylized shape.

The team eventually found a middle ground: they created real hair for Tracer but also preserved its unique shape. "There was just a lot of exploration as far as 'How far do we want to get away from the game art?'" said Chamberlain. "It needed, at a glance, to feel like it was the game, but if you put everything side by side, there's clearly a difference."

Another major difference was the characters' 3D models. Using *Overwatch*'s concept art as inspiration, the team explored how the characters should look in the game and the cinematic.

"When we compared the models, we realized that there was a lot of variety in how they were expressed," said Chamberlain. For example, one version of Tracer featured long, thin legs, closely matching her stylized look in the concept art, while another exploration depicted her with shorter legs and more realistic proportions.

The team ultimately combined elements from both interpretations into the final versions of the characters. In Tracer's case, they adjusted her model to preserve the stylized legs in her concept art.

THIS PAGE Sketches exploring the level of detail in Reaper's outfit and weapons.

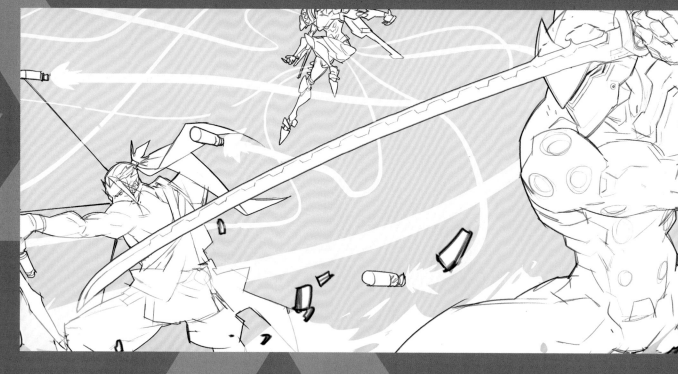

OVERWATCH FIRST VICTORY

THESE PAGES Storyboards fleshing out the details of the announcement trailer.

TOP RIGHT Early version of line art for an illustration.

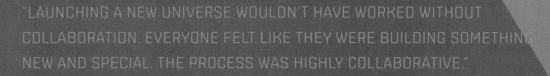

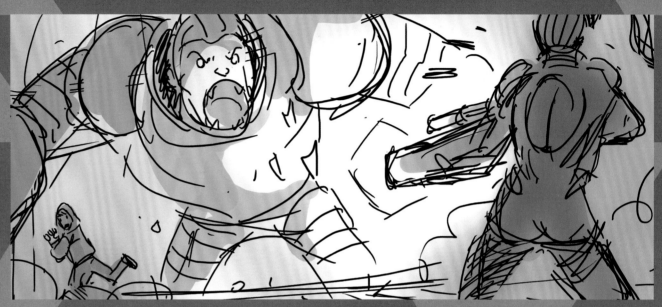

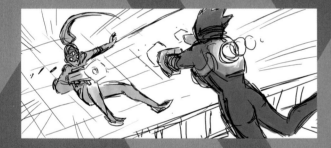

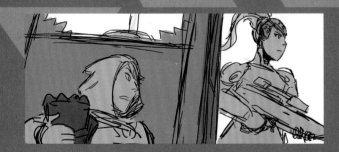

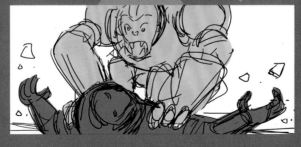

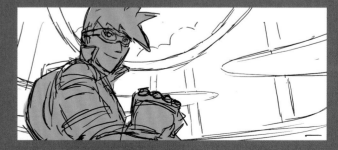

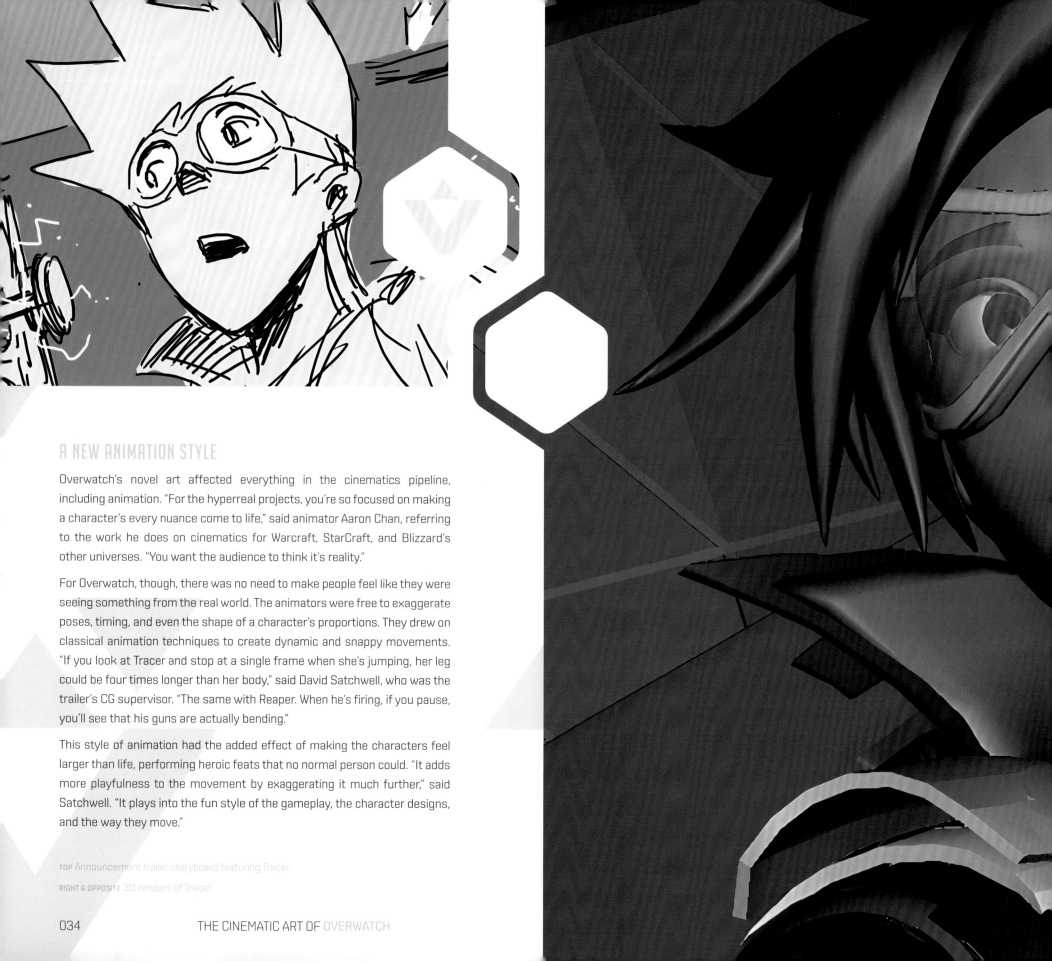

A NEW ANIMATION STYLE

Overwatch's novel art affected everything in the cinematics pipeline, including animation. "For the hyperreal projects, you're so focused on making a character's every nuance come to life," said animator Aaron Chan, referring to the work he does on cinematics for Warcraft, StarCraft, and Blizzard's other universes. "You want the audience to think it's reality."

For Overwatch, though, there was no need to make people feel like they were seeing something from the real world. The animators were free to exaggerate poses, timing, and even the shape of a character's proportions. They drew on classical animation techniques to create dynamic and snappy movements. "If you look at Tracer and stop at a single frame when she's jumping, her leg could be four times longer than her body," said David Satchwell, who was the trailer's CG supervisor. "The same with Reaper. When he's firing, if you pause, you'll see that his guns are actually bending."

This style of animation had the added effect of making the characters feel larger than life, performing heroic feats that no normal person could. "It adds more playfulness to the movement by exaggerating it much further," said Satchwell. "It plays into the fun style of the gameplay, the character designs, and the way they move."

TOP Announcement trailer storyboard featuring Tracer.

RIGHT & OPPOSITE 3D renders of Tracer.

"WHAT OVERWATCH HELPED US DO IS TRANSFORM FROM A MODEL-CENTRIC STUDIO INTO A PERFORMANCE-CENTRIC STUDIO."

—HUNTER GRANT, LEAD ANIMATOR

BALANCING EFFECTS

For past cinematics, the team had used every technological tool at their disposal to create highly detailed and realistic special effects. Overwatch called for something different. "The effects are much more simplified, almost like a 2D hand-drawn look," said surfacing supervisor Steven Chen. When creating things like muzzle flashes or ricocheting bullets, more focus was put on stylized colors and shapes than photo-realism.

The key for the filmmakers was finding a balance—a level of detail that would look good in the trailer and leverage the team's technology while also preserving Overwatch's stylization. This led them to approach different kinds of effects in different ways. "If it was a character effect, something like Winston's jump pack or his Tesla Cannon, we would try to mimic that as close to the game as possible because it was iconic," said CG supervisor Shimon Cohen.

At the other end of the effects spectrum were explosions. "For cinematics, they have to be done through fluid simulations," said Cohen. "They're dynamic and very much based in realism." Using simulations prevented the team from changing how the explosions formed and moved. However, they were able to simplify textural details and the amount of debris thrown out by an explosion to align more closely with the Overwatch aesthetic.

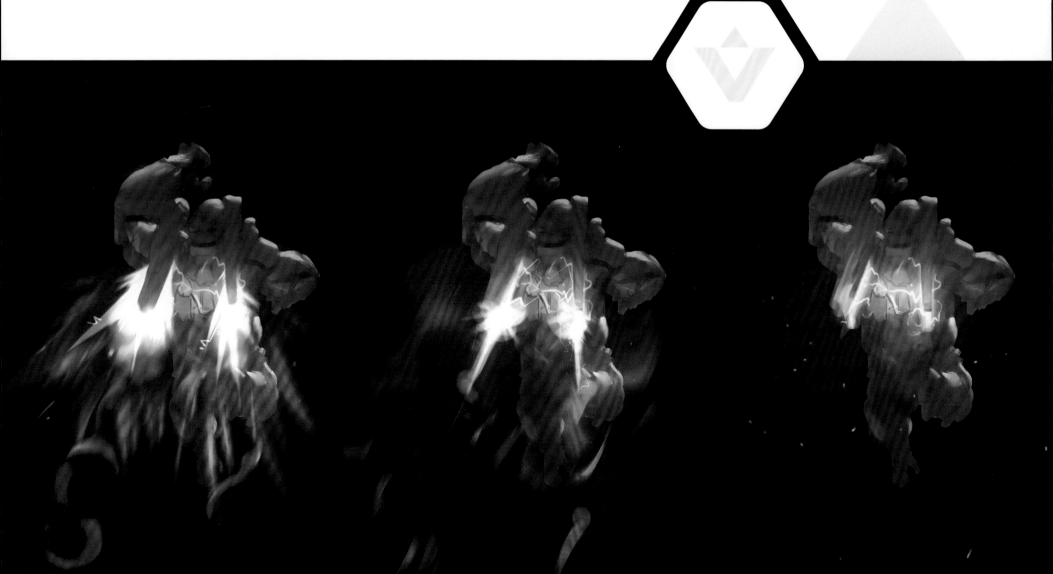

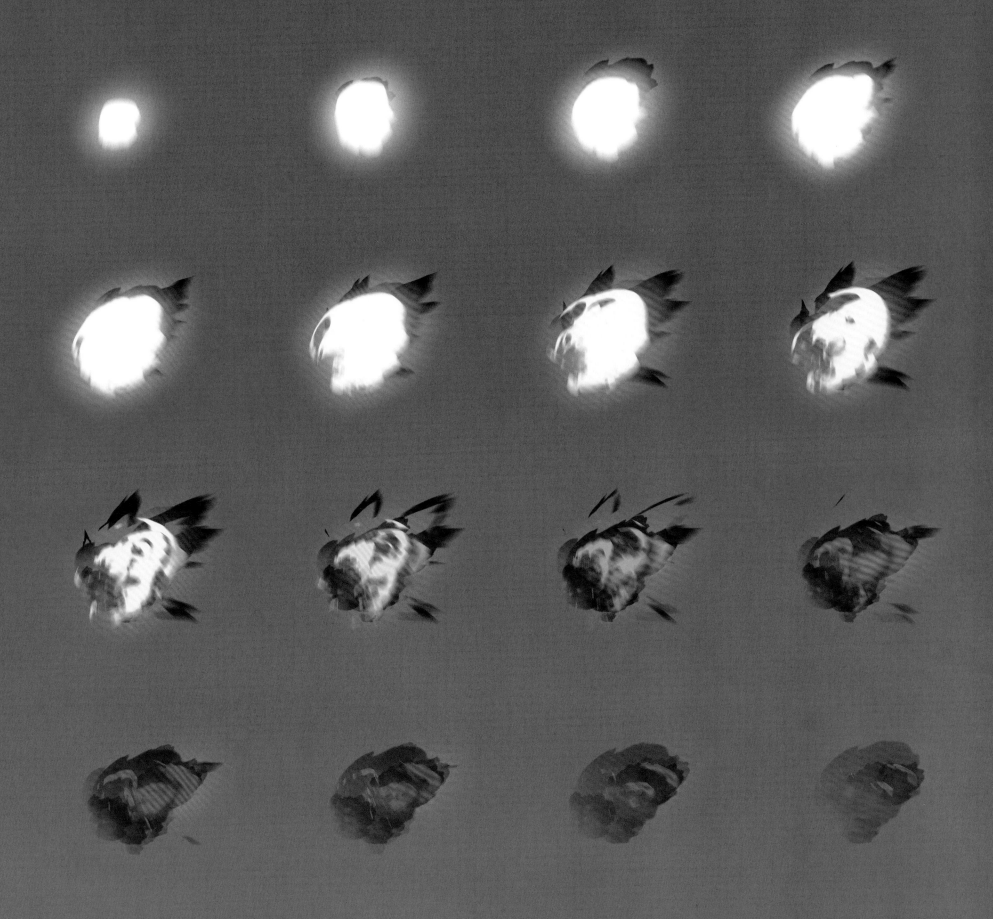

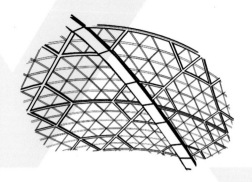
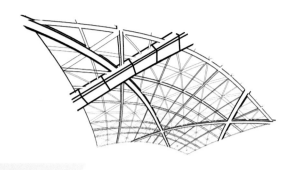
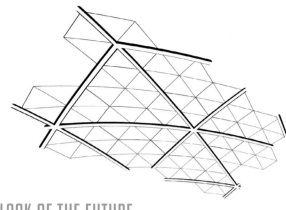

THE LOOK OF THE FUTURE

The museum was the first location in the Overwatch world that anyone would see, and that made every detail matter. What kind of architecture would characterize the future? What was the level of technology? How should light and color reflect the tone and themes of the game?

In early meetings, ideas revolved around giving the museum a more traditional look since it was a place devoted to history. But this seemed to miss a major opportunity to introduce the audience to the world outside the museum's walls. "We didn't have a lot of opportunities to sell the modern and futuristic aspect of things," said Belin.

Consequently, conveying how advanced the Overwatch universe is became mandatory for the museum's design. Artists fleshed out different versions of the building, trying to capture the right sense of scale, illumination, and clarity. These early concepts depicted a large open area with ample natural light.

However, the simplicity of the modernized museum—a predominantly white space with scarce detail—presented a challenge: How do you make it interesting? "What is a museum or an exhibition if there is nothing to see in it?" said Belin. "The way we approached it was more like an art space. The emptiness is a part of it. Since we couldn't have a million little props around, we decided it would be better to display massive props to give a sense of awe."

The shapes of the walkways and staircases, and even the latticework windows on the roof, added much-needed depth to the location while still leaving enough room for Tracer, Winston, Widowmaker, and Reaper to engage in a dramatic confrontation.

Color was also key to making the museum vibrant and dynamic. The team determined that even shadows would have subtle hues to them—a decision that would influence lighting choices in future cinematics. But they were careful not to oversaturate the environment. "We play a lot with contrast of color," said Chen. "If you isolate certain colors in a single frame of the cinematic, they aren't saturated. But when you put them all together, they feel saturated because of the contrast."

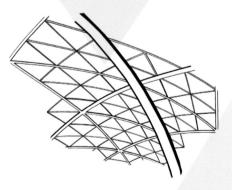
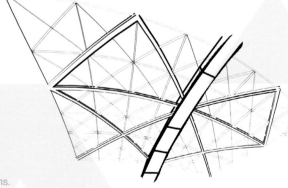

TOP & BOTTOM Sketches of the museum's roof patterns.

MIDDLE Exploration of the museum's lighting and color.

OPPOSITE Concepts of a drone displayed in the museum.

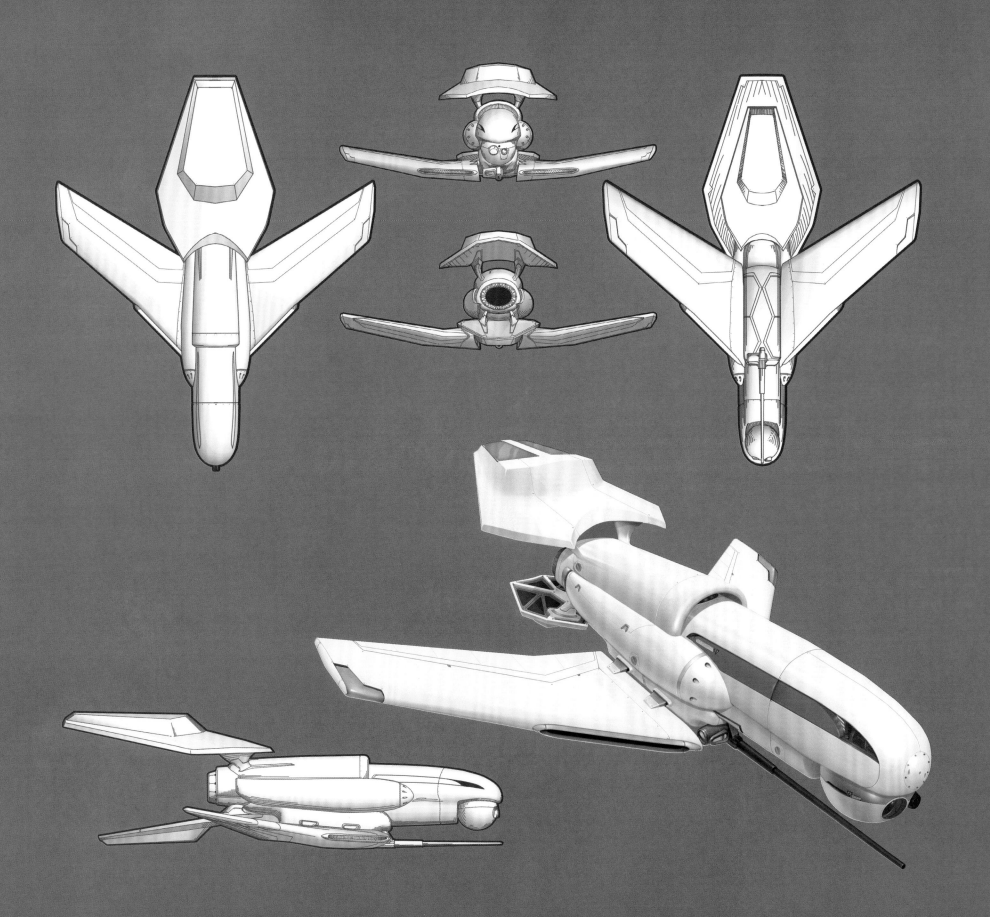

THE HEART OF THE STORY

Even with all the attention paid to the museum setting and the starring cast of heroes and villains, the trailer's success still hinged on the kids—internally referred to as "Brian" and "Timmy." They were the heart of the piece, and their point of view would be the audience's window into this new world. If the cinematic was going to have an emotional impact, the characters would need to be relatable and likable. Personality, voice acting, and animation were all crucial components, but an equally important piece of bringing Brian and his younger brother, Timmy, to life was *how* they looked.

"We definitely struggled in the beginning," said Chen. "Because the characters were young, they didn't have wrinkles or other facial details that artists would normally be able to work with."

Early versions of the children didn't feel like real people. Part of the issue was that light wouldn't penetrate their skin, which made them look like plastic or resin statues. Artists made the 3D models much more translucent than normal to give the characters the flesh-and-blood look they were trying to achieve. They also added other subtle touches to breathe life into the brothers and make it easier for audiences to identify with them and—by extension—the world of Overwatch. For example, the team created a bit of redness around Timmy's eyes and nose and made his hair softer and shinier.

"Kids, they're perfect, you know," said Belin. "Their hair is shiny and strong; their faces don't show any of the traces of aging. We wanted to make them visually pure, especially Timmy, as a reflection of his character. He's the innocence of the piece."

THIS PAGE Explorations of the look of "Timmy" and "Brian" through sketches and 3D models.

OPPOSITE Paint-over of a 3D version of "Brian."

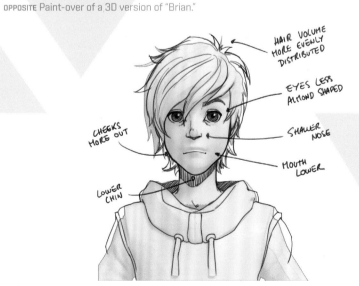

HAIR VOLUME MORE EVENLY DISTRIBUTED

EYES LESS ALMOND SHAPED

CHEEKS MORE OUT

SMALLER NOSE

MOUTH LOWER

LOWER CHIN

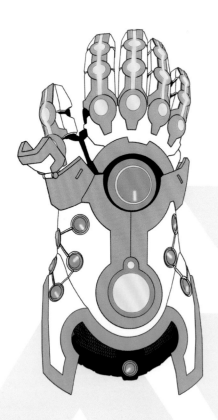

BZZZ...
"POWERING UP"

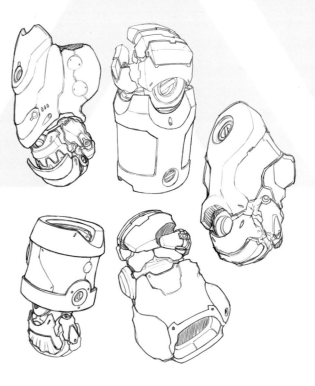

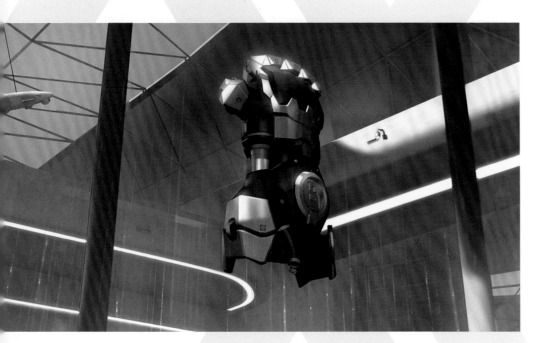

THE DOOMFIST GAUNTLET

▲ Early in production, a big question the team wrestled with was why a fight would break out in the museum at all. What is it that Tracer and Winston are stopping Widowmaker and Reaper from doing? "It couldn't be that there was just a fight blowing through town," said Chamberlain. "So we decided that there was some artifact there that the villains wanted."

And that was how the Doomfist gauntlet was born. The item was merely a storytelling device—a reason for the heroes to converge on the museum. Only later would the Doomfist character be added to the game and become an important part of Overwatch's story.

In the absence of a character attached to the Doomfist gauntlet, the process of finding the right look for the artifact revolved around the story needs and the surrounding museum aesthetics. Some of the early concepts were too fantastical. Others felt too much like robotic arms. Gradually, the team homed in on a version that felt like something a human could use but that also wasn't too overburdened with detail.

"We wanted there to be more mechanical elements to support the idea of the knockout punch," said Tsang, referring to the moment when the Brian character dons the gauntlet and uses it to knock Widowmaker across the museum. ▼

ABOVE & OPPOSITE Early concepts of the Doomfist gauntlet.

LEFT Final design of the gauntlet.

FOLLOWING PAGES Illustration for the announcement trailer.

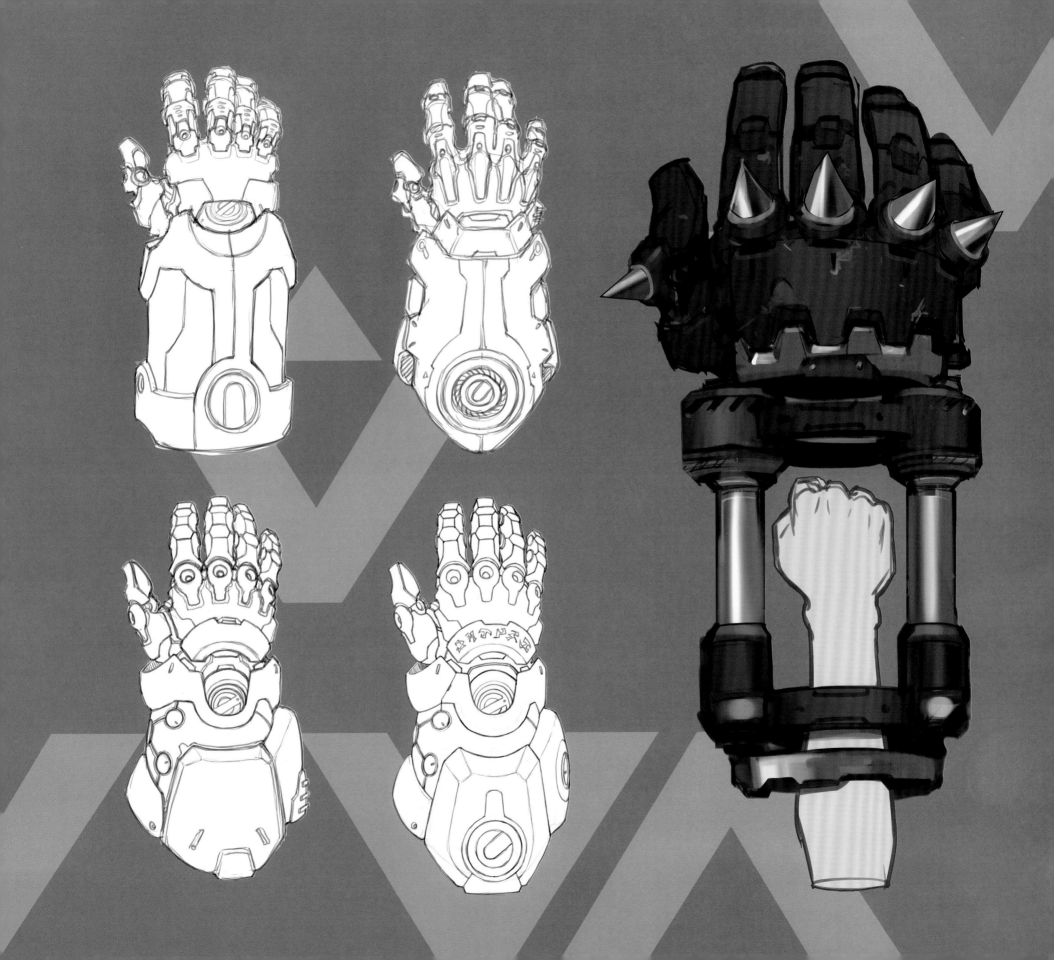

WE ARE OVERWATCH

"WE ARE HOPE. WE ARE HONOR. WE ARE COURAGE. WE ARE JUSTICE. WE ARE COMPASSION. WE ARE DETERMINATION. WE ARE HARMONY. WE ARE OVERWATCH."

—THE HEROES OF OVERWATCH

RIGHT Color key exploring the vignette of Tracer in Numbani.

AFTER THE ANNOUNCEMENT TRAILER, THE TEAM STARTED A

smaller but equally ambitious project called "We Are Overwatch." Just under a minute long, the piece would play before *Star Wars: The Force Awakens* at movie theaters around the United States in the winter of 2015, giving audiences a glimpse of the characters, world, and themes of the yet-to-be-released game.

Instead of telling a traditional story as in the announcement trailer, "We Are Overwatch" was conceived of as a montage. Set to a rousing score, it features short vignettes of Overwatch's iconic characters as they battle mechs and protect innocents from danger. Every scene says something about who the heroes are and what the world of Overwatch is like.

Because the vision for "We Are Overwatch" was so distinct from the announcement trailer, the supporting development process was also different. There were almost no storyboards created after the team brainstormed ideas for the shots. Rather, art director Stephan Belin immediately began painting one image per vignette to convey the lighting, tone, and composition. "Normally things would shift around more throughout production," said Belin. "But this one was different. The shots looked very close to how they were painted in the very beginning."

The only exception to this process was the shot with Genji. While the team had a clear idea for how to represent the other characters, he remained an enigma. What kind of single image would express who he is but still feel unique alongside the other characters' vignettes?

Owen Sullivan, one of the storyboard artists, took a stab at it. The scene he came up with is undeniably Genji. Pink cherry blossoms—a nod to the character's Japanese heritage—drift around him as he sits in a tranquil pose atop a giant enemy mech he has just sliced to pieces. Everyone on the team loved the idea. From there, Belin painted over the storyboard, adding more color and texture.

LEFT Storyboard for the Genji vignette.

SMOOTH TRANSITIONS

Every vignette in "We Are Overwatch" featured a lighting scheme and color palette that was informed by its focus on character and location. But at the same time, the filmmakers wanted to create smooth transitions between these varied settings.

"After the paintings for the shots were made, I shuffled them around so that there would be a nice succession," said Belin. "Sometimes you go from super colorful to drab, from bright to dark, and it can be quite jarring. So that was one of the things we needed to make sure of—that we could retain a sense of coherence between the shots."

ABOVE Concept of the thug.

RIGHT Color keys of assorted vignettes.

OPPOSITE, TOP Concepts for the extra that appears in "We Are Overwatch" and "Alive."

OPPOSITE, BOTTOM Color key for the Mercy vignette.

FOLLOWING PAGES Color key of the D.Va vignette.

EXTRA FROM "ALIVE"

▲ During the development of "We Are Overwatch," director Jeff Chamberlain saw some secondary character concepts created for the "Alive" short, which had just started production. He picked one of the designs, an anonymous female human, to feature in a "We Are Overwatch" vignette. The scene, set in London, shows the armor-clad hero Reinhardt shielding the woman and her omnic companion from a fiery explosion.

What Chamberlain didn't know was that Jeramiah Johnson, the director of "Alive," had picked the same extra for a role in that project, where she is also accompanied by an omnic during an event that takes place in London.

Ultimately, the unintentional coincidence worked out. "We realized it could just be the same person in the same world," said Chamberlain. ▼

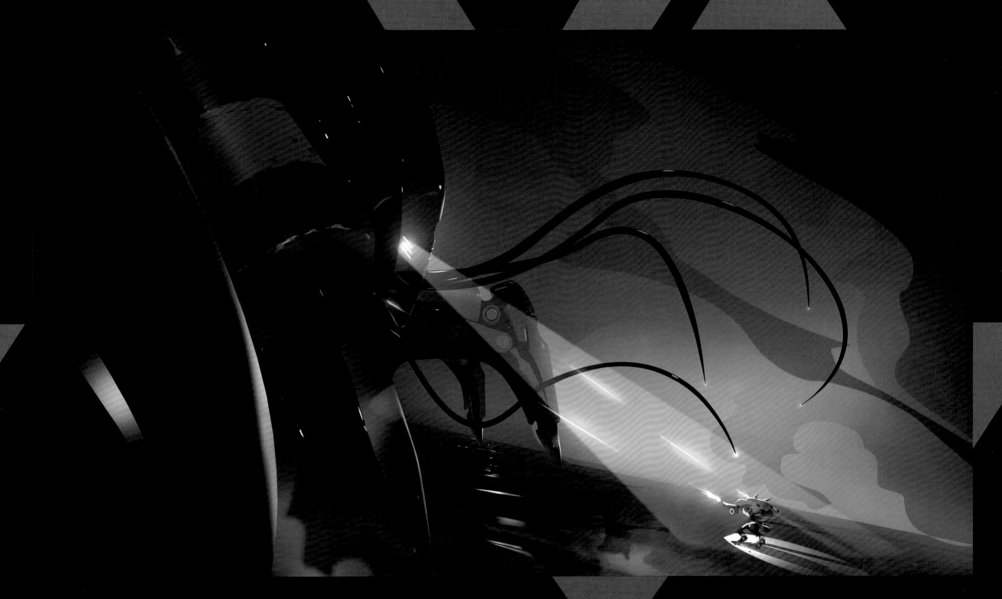

DESIGNING THE RIGHT ENEMY

"I FIND THAT BACK AND FORTH REALLY REWARDING, WHERE WE TAKE THINGS THAT HAVE BEEN DONE IN THE GAME AND PUT THEM IN THE CINEMATICS AND VICE VERSA."

—HUNTER GRANT, LEAD ANIMATOR

ABOVE Early design for the mech in the D.Va vignette.

OPPOSITE In-progress artwork depicting the mech in the D.Va vignette.

▲ The team changed the enemy mech in D.Va's vignette a few times before finding something that conveyed the right scale. "We needed it to tower above D.Va, but at the same time, the aspect ratio of the cinematic is fairly wide, so we also needed to have the legs crab-like or spider-like," said Belin. "The design was informed by how we would frame the shot."

The original concept art was too squat to give a clear sense of the scale. It also felt too much like a creature instead of a machine, which was a concern, as the giant mech needed to resemble omnics, sentient robots that are an important part of the Overwatch universe.

Belin blocked in the mech for the painting of D.Va's vignette to ensure it would have a clear silhouette that conveyed its size and mechanical origins. Artist Fabio Zungrone then created the design in 3D by reassembling elements from existing machine and omnic models. "The hope was that we would get something that really looked like Overwatch because it was made out of omnic parts and things like that," said Belin. "It worked out in the end." ▼

"THE PROCESS OF DOING THE ANIMATED
SHORTS FORCED US TO ASK CHARACTER
AND BACKSTORY QUESTIONS THAT WE
COULDN'T HAVE ASKED OTHERWISE."

—JAMES WAUGH, FORMER DIRECTOR OF STORY
    AND CREATIVE DEVELOPMENT

The scene with Pharah soaring over a battlefield sparked
discussions about depicting a character's powers in
cinematics. In the game, she could only fly for a short
period of time, but did that rule apply to other forms of
storytelling? Nothing had been set in stone yet—not
for Pharah or the other characters. The team decided
that because the animated shorts didn't have to take
game mechanics or player-versus-player balance into
consideration, they should have more freedom in how
they represent a character's abilities.

RECALL

"ALWAYS REMEMBER, NEVER ACCEPT THE WORLD AS IT APPEARS TO BE. DARE TO SEE IT FOR WHAT IT COULD BE."

—DR. HAROLD WINSTON

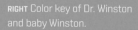

RIGHT Color key of Dr. Winston and baby Winston.

RELEASED ON MARCH 23, 2016, "RECALL" WAS THE FIRST

in a series of animated shorts that would continue fleshing out the world of Overwatch and build excitement for the game's upcoming release. Initially, the team considered doing a sequence of closely tied-together episodes that would tell a single, overarching story. But as brainstorming sessions continued, the story room decided that the best way to reveal more of Overwatch to audiences was with individual shorts told through the eyes of the game's heroes and villains.

"The narrative point of view on these shorts was really going to be about celebrating the characters and getting a window into who they were and what made them tick," said former director of story and creative development James Waugh, who cowrote "Recall" with senior writer Matt Burns. Through the characters, the cinematics would offer a glimpse into the broader universe of Overwatch. "That was exciting," said senior producer Phillip Hillenbrand. "It meant that we were finally able to do what the team had wanted to do for a long time: build really character-driven pieces."

The question then became *who* these shorts would be about. There was no shortage of interesting characters to choose from, but their points of view would need to be carefully matched to the specific stories the team wanted to tell.

For the first short, the premise was that someone would try to bring the disbanded Overwatch organization and its agents back together. "Who's the character who actually has a desire to do that?" said Waugh. "There were early conversations where we felt like Winston should be the launch point."

The highly intelligent gorilla, Winston, was one of the main heroes from the announcement cinematic, and he also symbolized many of the game's dominant themes. "We picked Winston because, in some ways ... he is the eternal optimist for Overwatch," said Jeff Kaplan, *Overwatch*'s game director. "He's the heart and soul of Overwatch."

Winston had developed his aspirational views while growing up on the Horizon Lunar Colony, where scientists had granted him extraordinary intelligence through gene therapy. Under the care of a kind human named Dr. Harold Winston, the gorilla learned to dream of a better future. And it was through Overwatch that he eventually found a way to make that dream a reality. After Overwatch's collapse, Winston took refuge in one of the organization's shuttered bases, Watchpoint: Gibraltar. There, he longed for a day when heroes would return to the world.

BELOW Early concept of baby Winston.

BOTTOM Color key of baby Winston in his room.

OPPOSITE Storyboards of Talon infiltrating Watchpoint: Gibraltar.

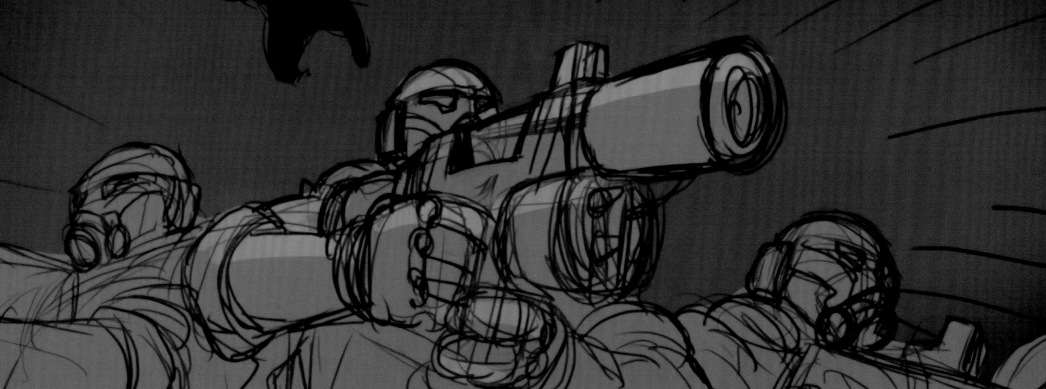

A NEW PROCESS

Transitioning from the announcement trailer to the character-driven shorts wasn't a seamless process. The plan was to make four new cinematics before the game's release in May 2016. With production on the shorts starting in the second half of 2014, that gave the team under two years to finish everything. They had never done anything like this before. Normally, it would take around a year to complete a single cinematic.

"It was us proving we can do this," said CG supervisor Shimon Cohen. "Proving we can do this to the level and expectations of what everyone would want. There were a ton of challenges with making sure that the animation and visual styles stayed true to the game."

Overcoming these challenges meant adopting new technology—such as a faster and more flexible rendering system called Redshift—and diverging from how they had approached making Overwatch's first cinematic. Instead of creating separate character assets, which the team had done for the announcement trailer, they pulled things like Tracer's 3D model right from the game engine and repurposed it for the animated shorts. Apart from slight adjustments to increase the complexity of the models, the assets in the cinematics are nearly identical to what people experience when they play the game.

"It was very important to stay in sync with the look and aesthetic of the game," said senior producer Kevin VanderJagt. "We wanted to see a correlation between game assets and cinematics. We wanted those to be close."

THIS PAGE Concepts for a Talon soldier.

OPPOSITE Early concepts for Reaper's hacking device.

WATCHPOINT: GIBRALTAR

One of the main settings for "Recall" is Watchpoint: Gibraltar. Unlike the museum in the announcement trailer, most of the location had been built for the game when production on the cinematic started, which gave the filmmakers a huge sandbox to play in. "We took a look at the map and identified a spot that could be Winston's laboratory and living quarters," said director Ben Dai.

From there, the team added visual elements, such as props, and began discussing how to light the set. "Isolation was a part of the design process," said Dai. "Ever since Overwatch disbanded, Winston has hidden in this base. He's only had one other person, the computer Athena, to converse with."

This sense of isolation is emphasized from the first shot. Signs that read "CLOSED BY EXECUTIVE MANDATE" and "KEEP OUT" hang on a chain-link fence, beyond which lies the dark and uninviting base. This introduction immediately reveals clues about the state of the Overwatch organization and conveys a sense of danger, loss, and abandonment.

However, the team also wanted to make Watchpoint: Gibraltar feel like Winston's home, one that was warm and inviting in its own way. The laboratory, strewn with tools and devices, hints at Winston's love of science. The computer station, bathed in the glow of holographic monitors, shows that he is continually keeping up with world events. Playing off his physical attributes, the team also designed a keyboard so that Winston could use his fingers or his toes to type. And the bananas and peanut butter jars scattered around the base ... well, everyone enjoys comfort food.

LEFT Color key for Watchpoint: Gibraltar.

VISUALIZING THE PAST

▲ One way the team made Watchpoint: Gibraltar feel like Winston's home was through the use of photographs. Snapshots of Winston at different ages standing alongside friends and family, like his mentor and former Overwatch agents, adorn the monitors of his workstation. The images depict moments of joy from the gorilla's life, things that he has lost over the years, and—in the case of Overwatch— ones that he is eager to reclaim.

But these photos did more than just allude to backstory; they helped define *how* photos should look in Overwatch. Including the images raised an important question: Should they be 3D, to match the rest of the cinematic, or 2D, to set them apart from current events? The team experimented with both, ultimately choosing the illustrative 2D approach, in large part because that style had been established in the short museum history video shown at the beginning of the announcement trailer. By drawing inspiration from the trailer, "Recall" strengthened this convention and influenced how future cinematics would present photographs or images from history. ▼

THIS PAGE Sketches of the Overwatch group photo in Watchpoint: Gibraltar.

OPPOSITE Early storyboards from the animated short.

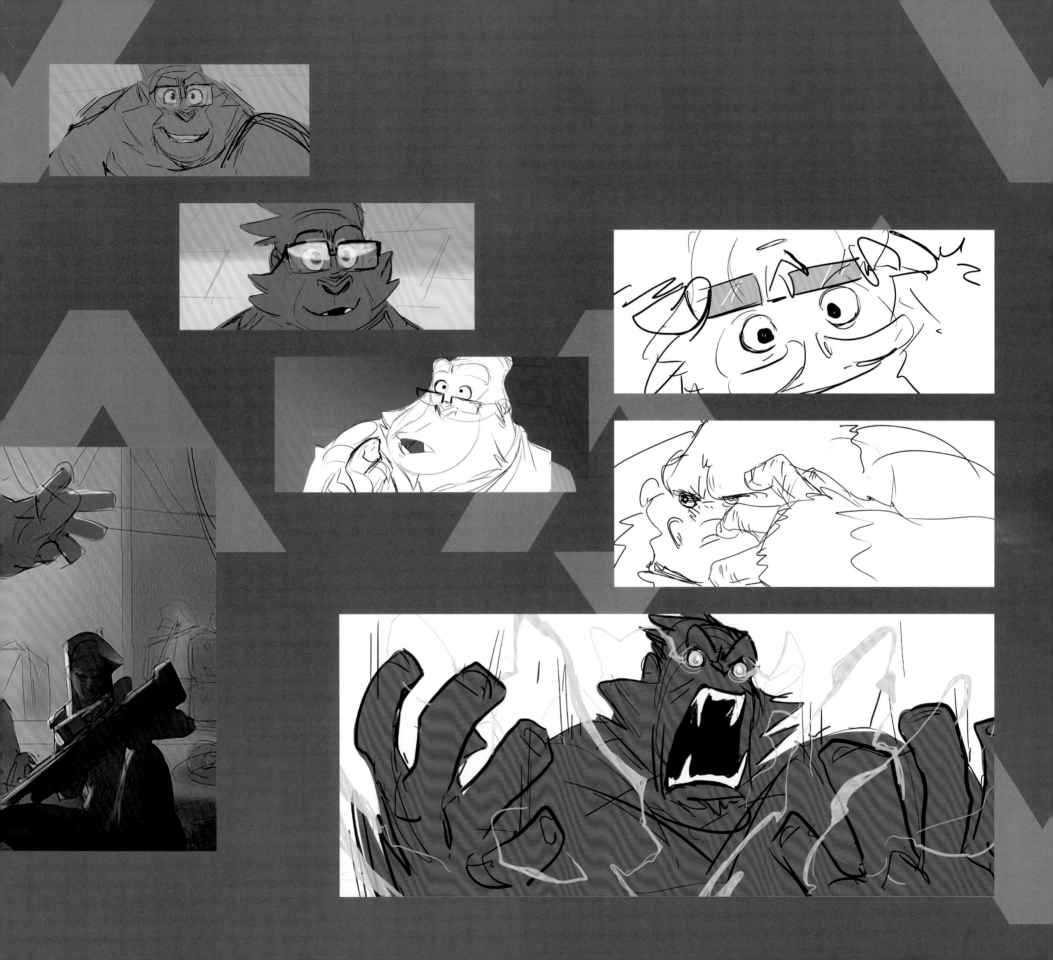

FLASHBACKS

Although the short used preexisting assets from the game, "Recall" also explored new settings and characters through flashbacks. Part of the story features Winston as a baby, which presented the filmmakers with an irresistible challenge: making him as cute as possible.

At first, the team considered creating geometric shapes for young Winston's fur similar to how hair had been modeled for other characters in the game. But after a few tests, it became clear the cuteness just wasn't there. The team departed from the established convention of creating solid, stylized hair and gave baby Winston fluffy—and adorable—fur.

But cute wasn't the only primary characteristic the team was chasing. Winston is a brilliant thinker, and the filmmakers wanted to acknowledge that by portraying the baby gorilla as curious and playful. Storyboard artist Haylee Herrick captured those qualities through facial studies that explored the range of young Winston's expressions. These sketches were then given to animators to use as reference—an important part of the production process that would continue in future cinematics.

The design of the Horizon Lunar Colony, which had not yet been made for the game, also needed to say a lot about who baby Winston was, just like how Watchpoint: Gibraltar mirrors the adult Winston's state of mind. After creating different pieces of concept art for the young gorilla's room, the team simplified the location and took out the messier elements to show how Winston, even as a child, had an ordered, focused mind. Props created for the room—a mix of toys and puzzles—visually hinted at Winston's personality and daily life.

One of these props, the lexigram poster hanging on the wall, was incorporated into Watchpoint: Gibraltar when the team transposed symbols from the chart on to a special keyboard for adult Winston's computer terminal, tying his upbringing to his current life. "The reason why I thought Winston might still use them later in life was that, one, it creates a connection to his past, and, two, I once read that the great scientist Richard Feynman had made up, as a child, his own mathematical symbols that he thought were better than the conventional ones," said art director Mathias Verhasselt. "I imagined that maybe Winston, similarly, made up his own system derived from lexigrams that he thought was better than what the humans used."

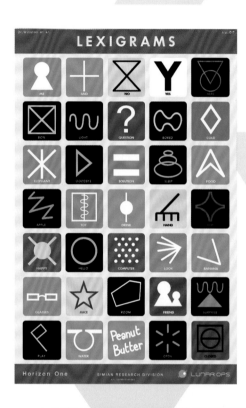

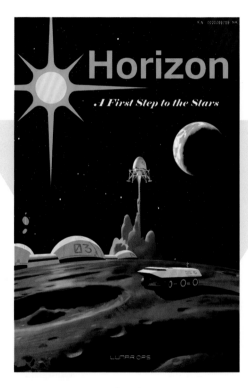

TOP Concepts of baby Winston.

ABOVE Lexigram and Horizon Lunar Colony posters.

LEFT Concept for baby Winston's room.

OPPOSITE Concepts of baby Winston.

PATCH ON LEFT ARM:

28
SIMIAN SPECIMEN
LUNAR OPS

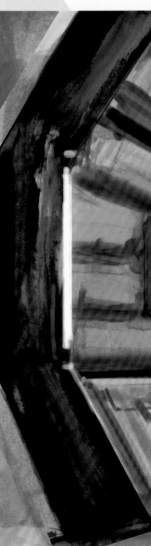

THESE PAGES Explorations of the hallway in the Horizon Lunar Colony facility.

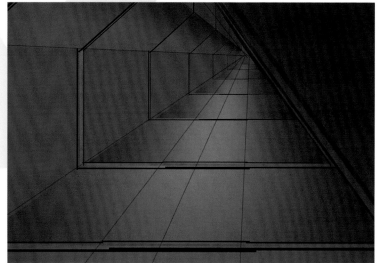

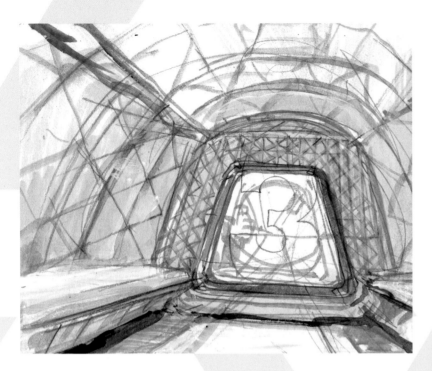

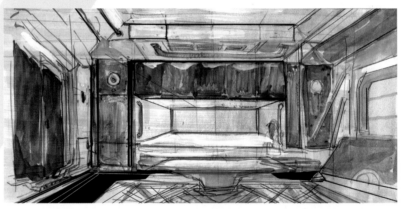

THESE PAGES Concepts created for baby Winston's room.

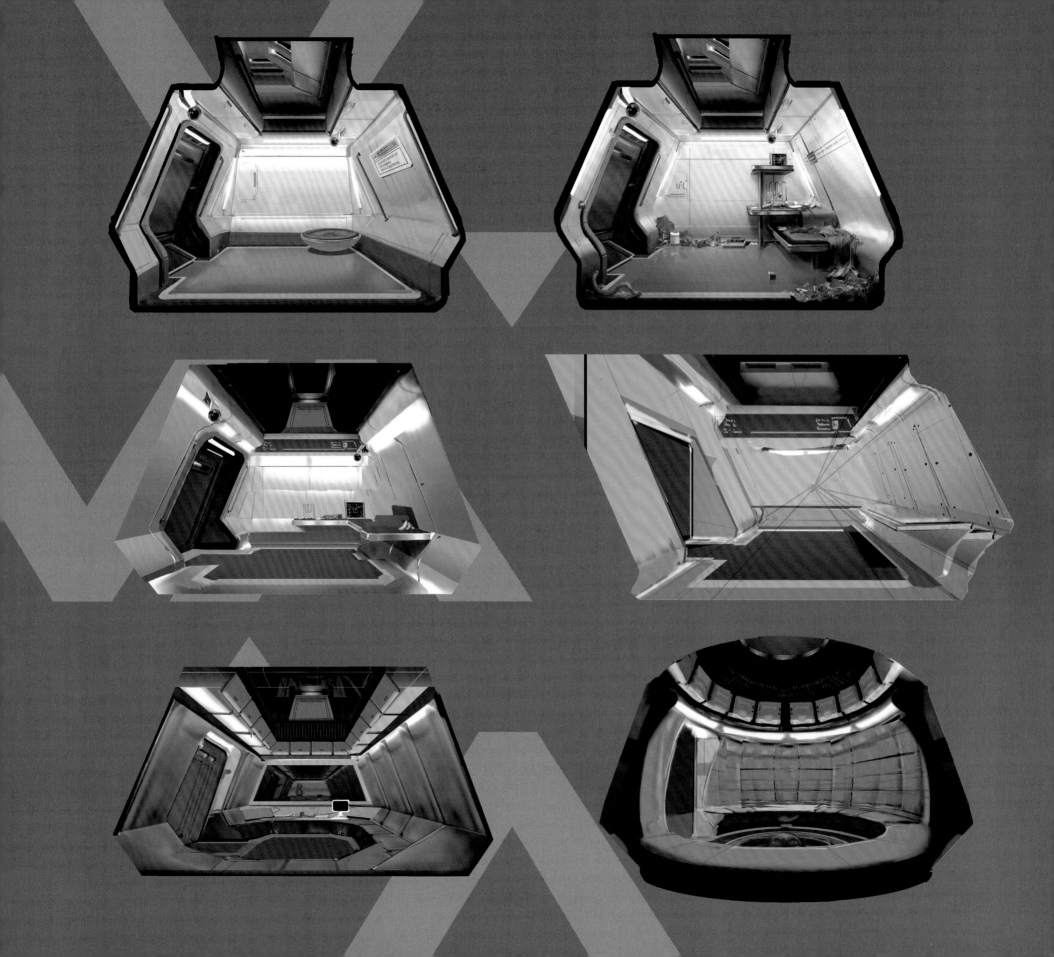

THE DEFINING MOMENT

Throughout production on the animated shorts, the team always searched for single images or moments that speak volumes about the world of Overwatch and its characters.

For "Recall," that image was Dr. Winston and baby Winston peering out of a lunar observation room at Earth in all its grandeur. "It was a defining moment for Winston and how he views the world," said senior producer Kevin VanderJagt. "It visually demonstrated why he is the way he is."

Complementing the image was a line spoken by Dr. Winston: "Always remember, never accept the world as it appears to be. Dare to see it for what it could be."

"That's the line that inspires him to push the button," said Kaplan, referring to the moment when Winston sends out a message to the former agents of Overwatch. "And that's the line that has come to sum up Overwatch."

RIGHT Color key for the Horizon Lunar Colony observation room.

COLOR AND EMOTION

▲ Color keys were an important part of finding the right look and feel for "Recall." Verhasselt sketched out these key images and then passed them on to other members of the team to serve as references for lighting and tone. "We chose to go with a darker version of the Gibraltar location, with cold colors and small islands of light around Winston's computers to emphasize his loneliness," said Verhasselt. "As a contrast, the flashback scenes are warm, faded, and nostalgic. The choice of typography, design language, and color scheme is reminiscent of sixties space futurism."

The color keys also acted like a visual chart to track emotions throughout the film. "In the beginning of the short, the feeling might be nostalgic, so we put in a lot of blues to draw out that vibe," said Dai. "When danger comes, it might be darker. When Winston's imagining a flashback, it's very bright and almost a bit dreamy." ▼

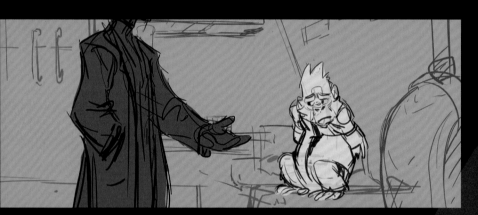

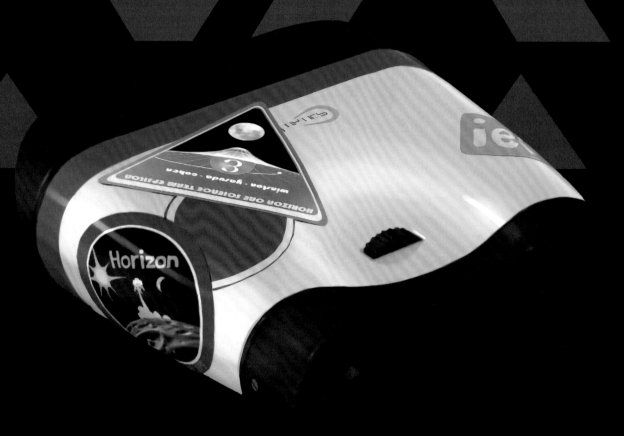

For the audience's first glimpse of baby Winston, the cinematics team wanted to show that the character was yearning to discover if something more was out there beyond the desolate lunar landscape where he lived. Early versions of the script called for the character to peer out of a window in his room through binoculars, but this idea was tabled in favor of having him use Dr. Winston's glasses. This change created an instant connection between the two characters and gave the team a way to reveal Dr. Winston's name that didn't feel forced or unnatural. When the scientist takes the glasses from the baby gorilla, his nametag briefly comes into focus through the lenses.

OPPOSITE, LEFT Early storyboards for the animated short.

OPPOSITE, RIGHT Color keys depicting important moments.

RIGHT Concept of binoculars used by baby Winston in an early version of the story.

BELOW Explorations of the Horizon Lunar Colony emblem.

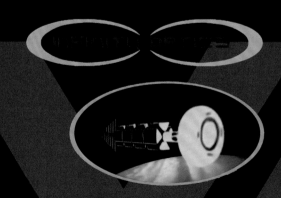

Winston's workstation, which was already present on the game map, was given an overhaul to make it more complex so it would seem like Winston is keeping tabs on *every* corner of the world. Many of the extra monitors added by the team were holograms or hard-light surfaces—things that could be turned off or on, which explains why they might not be visible in the game's version of the map.

LEFT Color key of Winston in Watchpoint: Gibraltar.

ALIVE

"WHEN I WAS A GIRL, I HAD A FEAR OF SPIDERS. I WAS TOLD THEY FELT NO EMOTION, THAT THEIR HEARTS NEVER BEAT. BUT I KNOW THE TRUTH. AT THE MOMENT OF THE KILL, THEY ARE NEVER MORE ALIVE."

—WIDOWMAKER

RIGHT Exploration of Widowmaker's visor point of view.

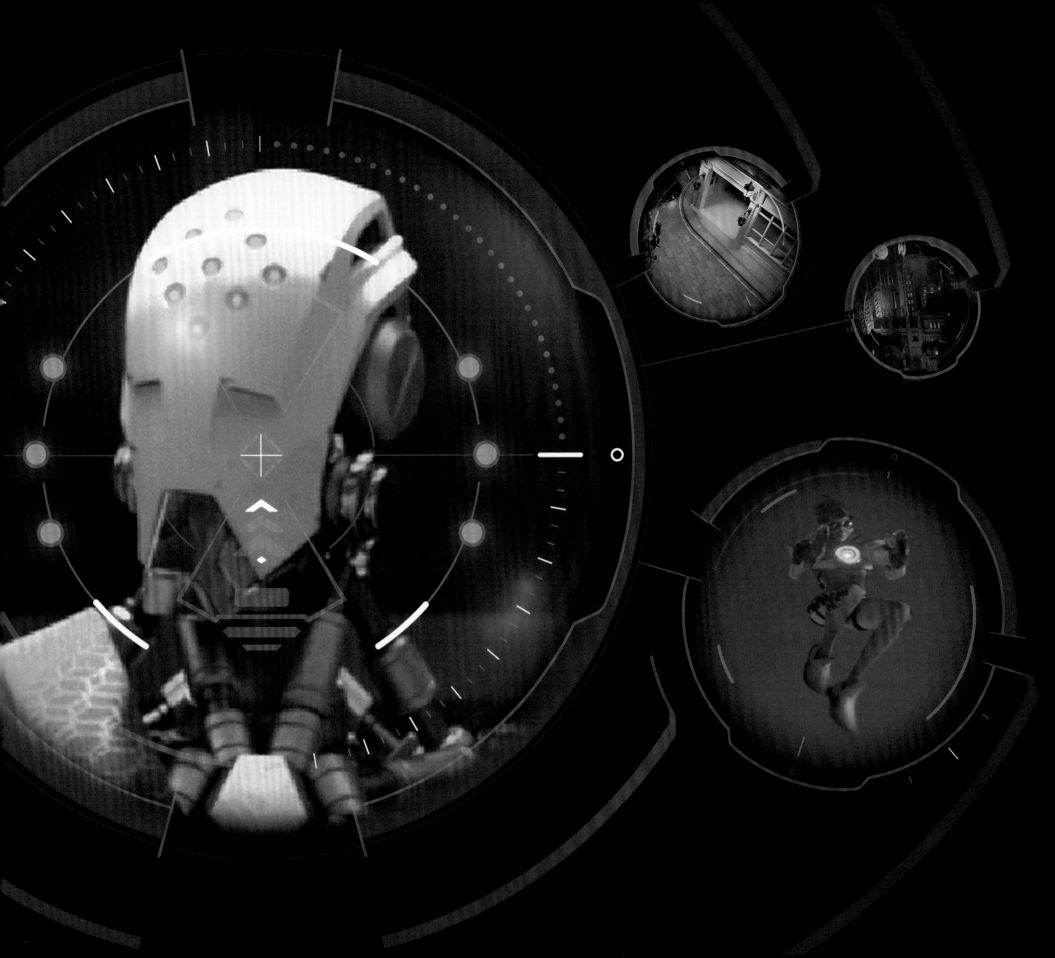

"ALIVE" WAS A JOURNEY INTO A DARKER SIDE OF OVERWATCH.

"We painted this world of a better future, a better tomorrow," said director Jeramiah Johnson. "But we also wanted to discover, 'How dark do we want to go in this world?'"

Released on April 5, 2016, the short follows the assassin Widowmaker as she stalks across London's rooftops, bent on bringing chaos to the city—and the entire world. Her target: Tekhartha Mondatta, an omnic dedicated to promoting peace between his kind and humans.

In an effort to start fleshing out Overwatch's broader universe, "Alive" introduced audiences to omnics and their struggles. Omnics—intelligent, sentient robots—live alongside humans, but tensions between them can run high. Decades ago, a terrible war between machines and humans called the Omnic Crisis had brought the world to its knees. The Overwatch organization was formed to end the conflict, but the war had left permanent scars on the hearts and minds of humans and omnics alike. In places like London, omnics face persecution from humans.

It was important to establish these concepts, partly because they would inform future stories and partly because they would usher audiences from the smaller, more contained locations featured in previous cinematics into the wider world of Overwatch.

"Each animated short was not only supposed to explore one of the heroes but also really illustrate part of Overwatch geographically and thematically—what it looks like and what it's like to live there," said Michael Chu, lead writer of *Overwatch* at the time.

THIS PAGE Concepts of human faces for the crowd attending Mondatta's speech.

OPPOSITE Explorations of clothing styles for the crowd.

DIVERSITY

For "Alive," the artists looked to Overwatch's diversity art pillar to create the crowd attending Mondatta's speech. Their goal was to demonstrate that people of all walks of life support omnics. "It was very intentional to make sure the crowd was diverse for many reasons," said Johnson. "One, we wanted to represent that theme, but also, in London, there's this tension between omnics and humans, where in other parts of the Overwatch universe, they get along."

This pursuit of diversity introduced a pair of challenges. Including dozens of unique characters on a single set wasn't possible given the time and resources the filmmakers had. Instead of creating new models for each human and omnic, the team reused versions of the same characters by outfitting them in different clothes.

The other challenge was the sheer amount of wardrobe needed for the large crowd. "How we were showing the crowd, it's mostly waist up," said Johnson. "So a lot of the variety we created was by changing jackets and headwear." It was also more efficient to change the color of clothes or add a different logo to a T-shirt than concept and model completely new wardrobes.

But what do clothes even look like in Overwatch's version of the future? Not much different from what people might wear today. The team wanted to make the clothing relatable to audiences. The familiarity of the wardrobes also helps keep attention on Tracer and other heroes, whose iconic, futuristic outfits set them apart from regular people.

In contrast to the humans, omnics either don't wear anything or were given jumpsuits to make them feel different from the humans wearing jackets, pants, and shirts.

THESE PAGES Concepts for the reporter Olympia Shaw, who was originally slated to appear in the short.

THIS PAGE Concepts for security guards at Mondatta's speech.

OPPOSITE Explorations of the interior and exterior of the Talon ship.

"HOW DO YOU GET A CHARACTER TO FEEL BELIEVABLE, TO CONNECT TO YOUR AUDIENCE, TO FEEL EMOTIVE, AND TO GET THE STORY ACROSS? THE TEAM WAS ABLE TO COME UP WITH A LOT OF VERY ELEGANT AND UNIQUE SOLUTIONS."

—HUNTER GRANT, ANIMATION SUPERVISOR

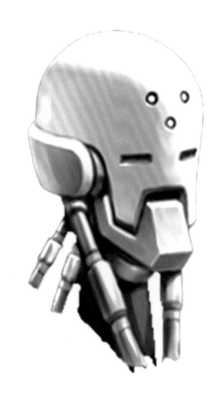

TOP Concepts for omnic facial features.

ABOVE & OPPOSITE Explorations of Mondatta's clothing.

DESIGNING MONDATTA

When production on the short started, Mondatta already existed as a statue in an early version of the King's Row map. However, much of his backstory had yet to be fleshed out. "There was no story about him really," said James Waugh, former director of story and creative development, who cowrote the piece with senior writer Matt Burns. "That came from the simultaneous development of the game and the short."

During the early stages of production, the team brainstormed ideas for Mondatta's personality and history to determine who the character is. They envisioned him as a force for good in the world—a wise and benevolent omnic who sought to create peace and harmony by bringing his kind and humans together.

Using the statue of Mondatta as a starting point, the team adjusted the character's design to reflect his identity. "We wanted to create a face that felt like it had presence and a gentleness about it. But we didn't want it to look completely like Zenyatta," said Johnson, referring to the game's playable omnic hero.

The team tried different color treatments for Mondatta's wardrobe to create something that felt regal and benevolent, but also distinct from Zenyatta's brown-and-red color scheme. A green-and-black palette came across as too villainous, out of sync with the character's message of love and hope. "Where we landed was actually more of a white with gold trim on his robes," said Johnson. This final design gave Mondatta an air of purity, which complemented the purity of his intentions to bring humans and omnics together.

Once Mondatta's design was locked for the cinematic, the statue on the map was changed to match it. "When people saw that statue in the game, they knew its significance and who the great omnic hero was," said Burns. "The statue had been in the map from the beginning, but now it was supported by a story, which gave it context and emotional impact."

FOCUSING ATTENTION

Many of Mondatta's supporters in the crowd wave signs emblazoned with images of human and omnic hands touching or messages of peace and unity, like, "We are all one in the Iris." These props served a dual purpose. Not only did they visually express the hopeful mood of the people attending the rally, they also helped the team engineer a dramatic entrance for Mondatta.

The filmmakers wanted the omnic to emerge from a large doorway at a theater on the game map and address the waiting crowd. The only problem was that the theater didn't have just one doorway; it had three. "That would be very distracting," Johnson said. "We wanted to create a single point of focus." By draping signs over the doorways on either side of Mondatta, the team was able to draw the viewer's eye directly to the character.

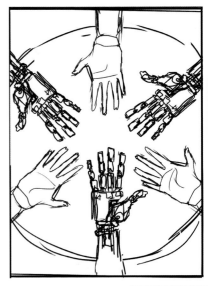

ABOVE & RIGHT Concepts for signs and banners held by the crowd and hung on the doors behind Mondatta.

OPPOSITE Concept of Mondatta delivering his speech.

FOLLOWING PAGES Storyboards of Mondatta and the crowd.

THE CINEMATIC ART OF OVERWATCH

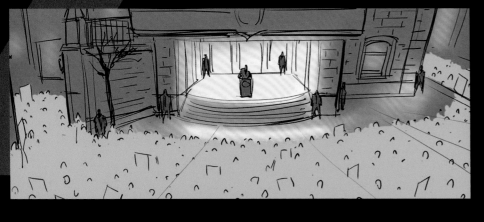

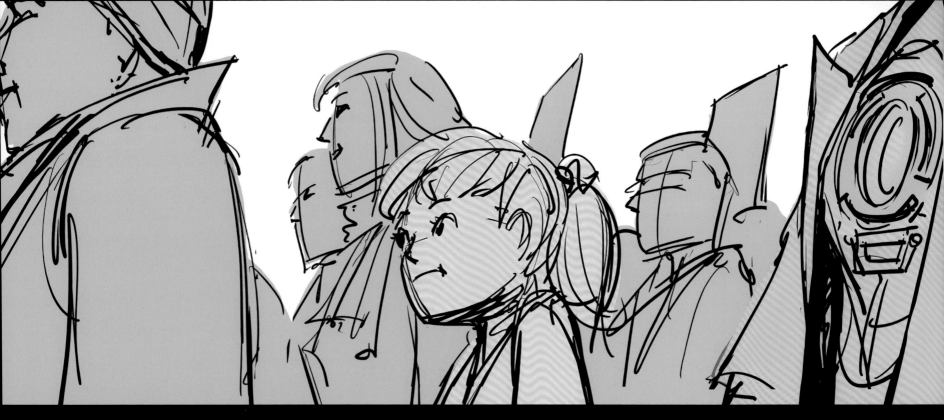
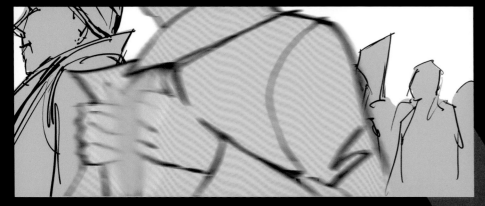

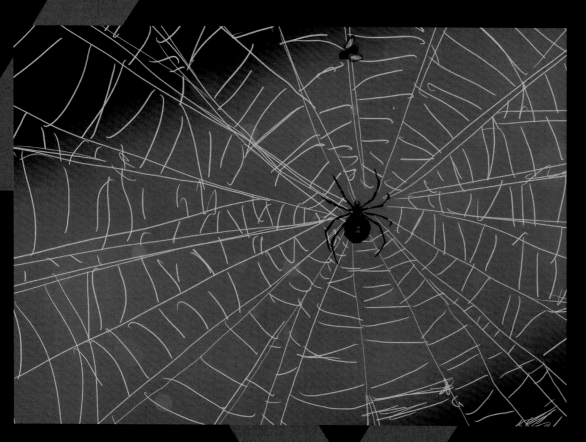

CONTRASTING CHARACTERS

When the story room first met to discuss the animated shorts, one of the things they focused on was the idea of pitting characters against one another in each piece. "There was a natural need to infuse the story with conflict," said Waugh. "It also gave us opportunities to showcase heroes and villains."

"Recall" focused on the hero Winston, but it also featured the masked villain Reaper. For "Alive," the story room wanted a similar duality between good and evil, but also a deeper psychological edge that went beyond just a physical battle. "Tracer was the clear thematic counterpoint to how Widowmaker looks at the world," said Waugh. "It was this bright optimistic view of hope and potential contrasted with someone who is completely cold and can only feel alive when she's breaking things."

Winston triumphed over Reaper in "Recall," but the same happy outcome wasn't in the stars for Tracer's battle with Widowmaker. "We knew that Widowmaker was going to win," said Johnson. "But we didn't want to telegraph it so much because we wanted it to have that impact of 'No. The heroes don't always win.' It was very intentional early on that we showed Tracer bubbly. 'I'm on the job. I can do this.' And then Widowmaker gets her. She finishes the job and gets away."

PREVIOUS PAGES Final render of Mondatta delivering his speech.

OPPOSITE Storyboard and color key of the spider and its web.

THIS PAGE Final images from the animated short.

EXPLORING EFFECTS

In "Alive," Tracer escapes a poison trap set by Widowmaker by using Recall, an ability that sends her zipping back through time. Although it was one of Tracer's signature moves in the game, how it would translate to the cinematic space had yet to be discovered.

"We don't see Tracer's Recall from her point of view, really," said CG supervisor Shimon Cohen. "We know technically she goes back in time. What would that look like? What does her chronal accelerator do? What is happening to her inside this little slipstream? Does everything reverse time? Or is it just her?" Asking these questions not only helped the filmmakers figure out how the ability should look in the cinematics but also what impact it would have on the characters and the surrounding world.

Ultimately, it was decided that only Tracer would be affected by the ability. That gave artists a direction to pursue. They focused their attention on Tracer and the particles that surround her as she slips into her time warp. "In the final cinematic, when the chronal accelerator starts to go, the sky turns more cyan," said Johnson. "When Tracer gets in front of Big Ben, you actually see the sky change back to its normal color because now we're back in the real world."

PREVIOUS PAGES Storyboards for key moments in "Alive."

THESE PAGES Explorations of Tracer's Recall ability.

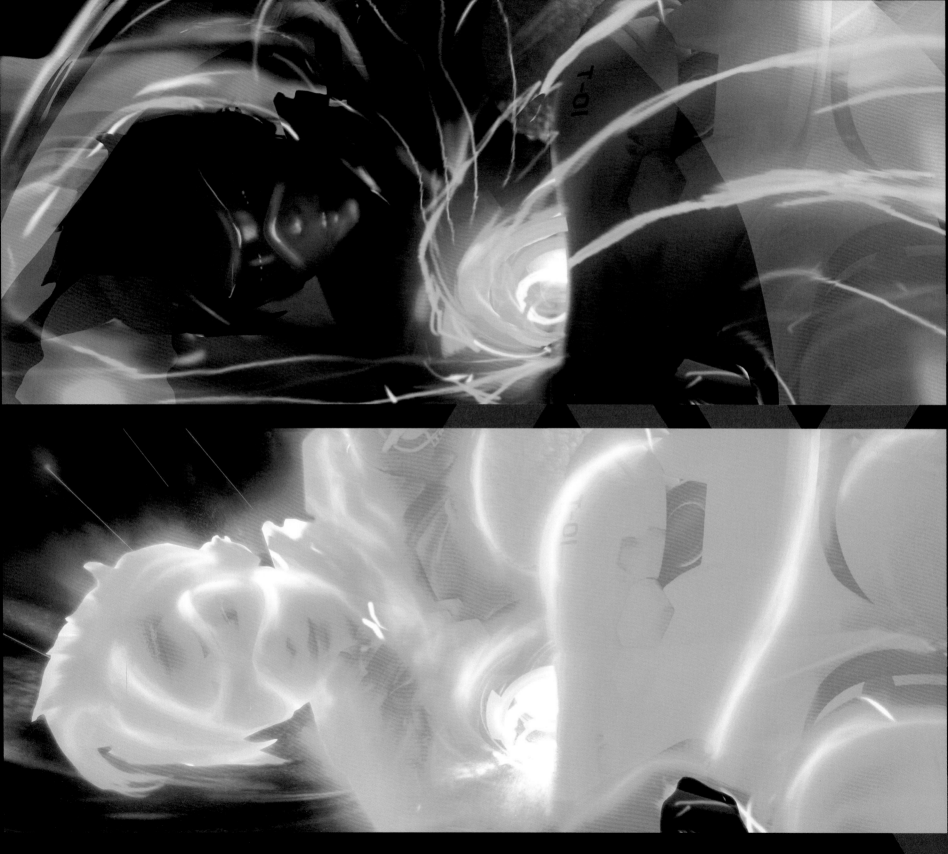

SETTING COLORS

▲ When the team was selecting locations on the King's Row map to stage the short, they experimented with the setting's color palette. In the game, the city is very orange at the street level while the futuristic skyscrapers that rise up in the distance are bathed in cyan.

"Originally, I came up with a very fiery color theme, a heavy cloud cover underlit by incandescent streetlights," said art director Mathias Verhasselt. This direction would have created a strong contrast with Widowmaker's cold blue color palette as she prowled the rooftops.

After further exploration, the team decided to adhere to what was already in the game in order to make the rooftops feel like Widowmaker's territory, a place where she can fade in and out of the shadows. "So we went with something similar but a bit darker, and slightly shifted toward greens to be more unsettling," said Verhasselt. ▼

THESE PAGES Explorations of Tracer's Recall ability.

DRAGONS

"I HAVE ACCEPTED WHAT I AM, AND I HAVE FORGIVEN YOU. NOW YOU MUST FORGIVE YOURSELF. THE WORLD IS CHANGING ONCE AGAIN, HANZO, AND IT'S TIME TO PICK A SIDE."

—GENJI

RIGHT Painting of the fairy tale from "Dragons."

RELEASED ON MAY 16, 2016, "DRAGONS" FEATURES HANZO AND GENJI,
two brothers with rich backstories. Scions of the Shimada family, their lives took a bloody turn when Hanzo was forced to kill Genji, his younger brother.

He did, or so he thought.

Unbeknownst to Hanzo, Genji survived and went on to become a member of Blackwatch, Overwatch's covert ops division, and then Overwatch itself. Hanzo, haunted by what he'd done, abandoned his family's legacy and set out to live his life as a solitary assassin.

"They each have a unique personality and something that makes them special," said senior producer Timothy Loughran. "It was exciting to have an opportunity to get in and establish a reason to care about them."

Bringing Hanzo and Genji face-to-face for the first time since their violent fracture provided an occasion to explore dark and disturbed emotions, as well as themes of absolution and redemption. The question that came up in the story room was how much of the brothers' backstory should be revealed—and through what techniques? Weaving flashbacks into "Dragons" seemed like a given, but the team wanted the short to feel distinct from "Recall," which had also featured flashbacks.

An idea that emerged in the story room was to allude to the brothers' history by evoking a fairy tale illustrated with Japanese-style paintings.

"This is a story their father would tell Hanzo and Genji at night, about the importance of family," said senior writer Andrew Robinson, who wrote the piece. "As you break from the action to the paintings, it affects the pacing in a wonderful way. It makes everything feel more legendary."

Storyboard artists created rough layouts of the parable and planned how the camera would move across the images in concert with voice-over narration. After that, the sketches were brought to life in greater detail. "We went through a few different versions of the illustrations before we reached something that captured traditional Japanese art but that also felt true to the Overwatch style," said director Ben Dai.

"This is the only time we've ever done that type of juxtaposition of imagery," said Robinson. "This actually provides emotional context to what the brothers are going through."

ABOVE Explorations of the art style for the fairy tale.

OPPOSITE & RIGHT In-progress art for one of the fairy-tale images.

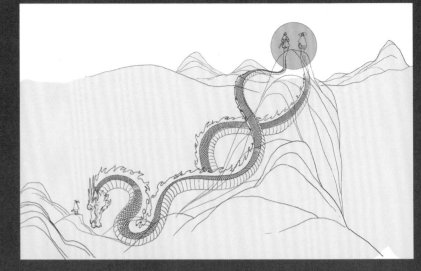

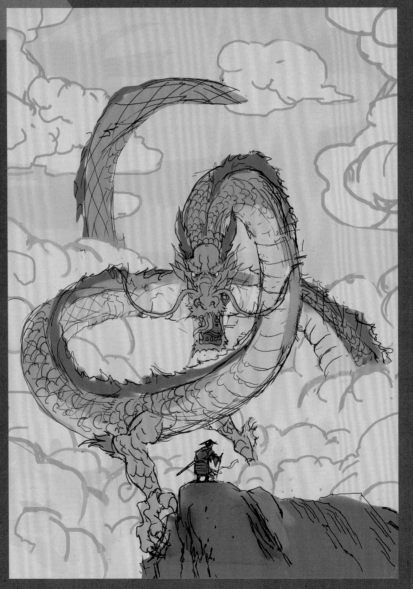

ABOVE & OPPOSITE, TOP RIGHT Explorations of different art styles for the fairy tale.

RIGHT In-progress layouts for the final images of the fairy tale.

OPPOSITE, TOP LEFT An early storyboard.

OPPOSITE, BOTTOM Full-color painting from the fairy tale.

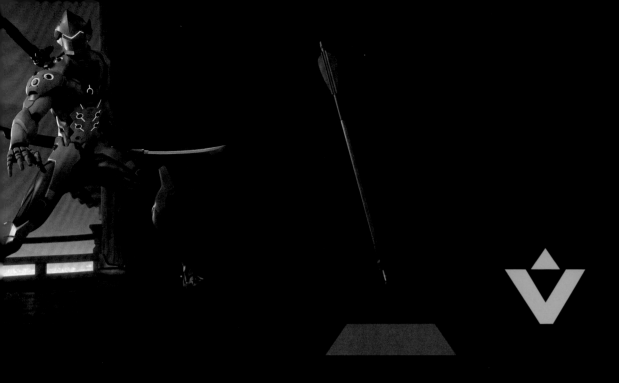

STORYTELLING ACROSS MEDIA

A damaged sword. A torn, bloodstained scroll. These were some of the scars left behind by the battle between Hanzo and Genji years ago—the battle that ended with Genji supposedly dead and Hanzo racked by guilt for what he had done. These details had been added to an early version of the Hanamura map to hint at the brothers' dark past.

During production on "Dragons," the map was updated to acknowledge the animated short, including shuriken and arrows embedded in the walls and floor. "If you saw the cinematic, these details would resonate with you ... they were a form of world-building to support the story," said *Overwatch*'s art director, Bill Petras.

ABOVE & RIGHT Stills from the short, depicting the interior and balcony of Shimada Castle.

DRAWING FROM THE SETTING

The Hanamura map's pink cherry blossom trees inspired visual and thematic elements in "Dragons." The blooming trees represent rebirth, which was an idea at the heart of the story as Hanzo and Genji's fateful meeting changes them both and begins a new chapter in their lives.

"Because the trees are featured so prominently in the game, we actually used the falling cherry blossom petals as a method of cross-dissolve between shots," said Dai. "There's one shot where there's a fire, and all the embers start turning into cherry blossom petals, and that reveals the next shot."

Art director Mathias Verhasselt also drew inspiration from the cherry blossom trees when making color keys for the short. Pink was woven into the sky to make the nighttime colorful and infuse the story with a hint of wonder. "The tale of brotherly conflict had a sense of storybook magic, which I tried to reflect in the lighting schemes, with the night mood transforming into a rosy predawn during the fight on the balcony," said Verhasselt.

THESE PAGES Color keys created for the animated short.

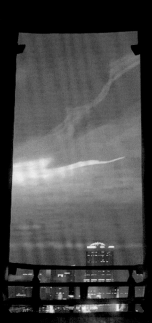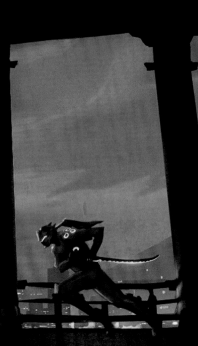

When creating concept art for the guards outside Shimada Castle, the team looked to real-life Japanese yakuza for inspiration. Artists added a Japanese *oni* mask to an omnic member of the criminal organization to make it look just as menacing—if not more so—than the human guards.

THESE PAGES Concepts for the Shimada Castle guards.

THESE PAGES Storyboards of the fight
between Hanzo and Genji.

FOLLOWING PAGES Painting of the fairy tale.

DUELING DRAGONS

At the climax of the short, Hanzo and Genji's duel spills onto the balcony,
where they unleash their ultimate abilities: Dragonstrike and Dragonblade.
The team wanted to mimic how these abilities appear in game as much as
possible, but some amount of change was inevitable.

"One thing that wasn't quite as apparent in the game was—where does
the dragon come from for Hanzo?" said CG supervisor Shimon Cohen. "The
original idea we had was that the tattoo itself would start lifting off of Hanzo
and become the dragon."

The team later settled on a variation of that idea: the dragon would rise from
the tattoo and start forming around Hanzo's arm, feeding into the tip of the
arrow before expanding into a massive vortex.

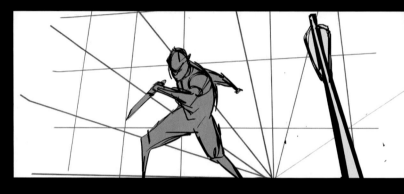

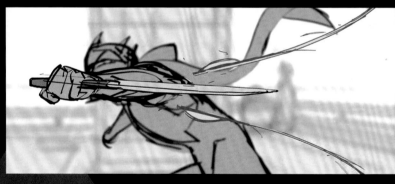

HANAMURA

▲ "Dragons" takes place in Hanamura, a Japanese city that had been created for the game before work on the animated short began. "It was really helpful to be able to go into the map, find the shots we wanted, capture images, and send them to the storyboard artists to draw over," said Dai.

The short spans the entirety of the map. Apart from adjusting the lighting from day to night, the only significant change the team made to the location was to extend a balcony just outside Shimada Castle. "At the end, most of the fighting happens inside the castle," said Dai. "There was plenty of space for the two characters to fight. But when we took it out to the balcony, that wasn't meant to be a big combat area, but we needed the huge dragon showdown."

To accommodate the finale, the team made modeling adjustments to the cinematic version of the location, extending the balcony to three times its normal size so that it would fit all the action, including the moment when Hanzo and Genji unleash their dragon-themed ultimate abilities. ▼

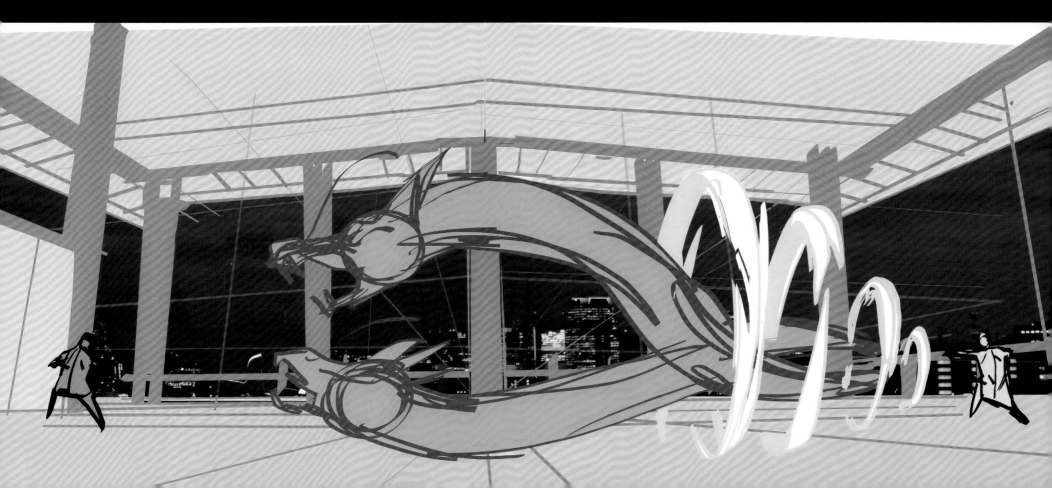

HERO

"OLD HABITS DIE HARD, I GUESS."

—SOLDIER: 76

 **RIGHT** Color key of Soldier: 76 in "Hero."

AT ITS HEIGHT, OVERWATCH WAS RUN BY STRIKE COMMANDER

Jack Morrison, a soldier who embodied the organization's courage, loyalty, and optimism. Under his guidance, Overwatch built a better future for the entire world.

And then everything fell apart. Overwatch came under investigation for human rights abuses, mismanagement, and other allegations. Its headquarters in Switzerland was destroyed in an apparent accident. Morrison was reported as one of the casualties. Overwatch didn't last much longer after that. The group was disbanded, its agents forbidden from using their powers to help the world, whether officially or unofficially.

What no one knew at the time was that Morrison hadn't really died. After Overwatch's collapse, he changed. He darkened. He became the masked vigilante known as Soldier: 76.

"He's driven to find out who was behind the fall of Overwatch and bring them to account," said senior writer Andrew Robinson, who wrote the "Hero" short.

Ironically, Morrison's tragic fall from grace was also a way to reinforce the franchise's hopeful themes. "It's about hanging on to optimism and believing in the possibility of a better world even with all the darkness around you," said Robinson. "Soldier: 76 is a guy who is kind of lying to himself. 'I *used* to be a hero.' But deep down, no matter what he thinks, in his blood, he is still a hero."

Telling a story with this theme—and about a character like Soldier: 76 who was so crucial to the lore—seemed like a fitting way to lead into the *Overwatch* game. The "Hero" cinematic was released on May 22, 2016, just two days before the game itself.

VISUAL METAPHORS

▲ Storyboard artists are always searching for key shots or moments that speak to the heart of a story. "That's the thing we live for. How do we visually show what's happening underneath the story?" said lead storyboard artist Mike Koizumi. "We add these visual metaphors that show it."

In "Hero," a key image like this appears near the end of the short when Soldier: 76 walks away from the camera and light slashes across the "76" on his back. First roughed out in storyboards, it was a moment that encapsulated the entire short by asking whether 76 stood in the light or in the darkness, whether he was good or bad. ▼

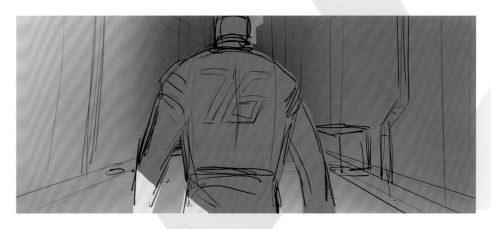

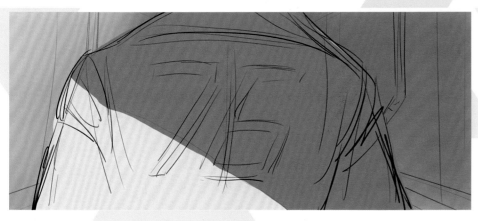

THES PAGES Early storyboards for key moments from the cinematic.

BODYTYPE A

BODYTYPE B

B1
"dark green"

B2
"green"

B3
"light green"

A1
"brown"

A2
"red"

A3
"orange"

A4
"yellow"

BODYTYPE C

LOS MUERTOS

In "Hero," Soldier: 76 is on a mission to stop the Los Muertos gang from smuggling weapons in Dorado. The idea for these villains and their luminescent tattoos originated from concept art created for the game. The team used this artwork as a foundation to design the small army of Los Muertos smugglers Soldier: 76 battles in "Hero."

The sheer number of characters presented a challenge to the time-pressed team. As with "Alive," they found creative ways to make many characters with limited resources. Two unique models—a skinny body type and an average body type—were built. From this pair of assets, the team created twelve visually distinct characters by giving them different combinations of tattoos, clothing, facial hair, and color.

C1
"dark blue"

C2
"blue"

C3
"light blue"

C4
"purple"

As with most of the other animated shorts, the team had a prebuilt location to work from: the Dorado game map. They also had the payload, a hovering truck used in the multiplayer version of the map, which they decided to incorporate into "Hero." The team repurposed the truck by removing some parts of the bed and adding modifications. The result was a vehicle the Los Muertos gang could use to transport their contraband guns, which were hidden inside piñata-filled crates.

OPPOSITE Concepts showing the variations of body type and clothing for the Los Muertos thugs.

THIS PAGE Color key depicting the city of Dorado.

BODY ART

▲ Luminescent tattoos were a defining visual trait for the Los Muertos gang, something that set them apart from ordinary thugs. From the beginning, the team was determined to showcase the tattoos, but getting the effect right proved challenging.

"We went back and forth on that a lot," said CG supervisor Shimon Cohen. "We had to really try to dial in where light and shadow hits the tattoo, even though it's illuminated, so you get shape and form within it."

In the later stages of production, the team added a glowing line around the tattoos to help give them more defined shapes. ▼

THESE PAGES Concepts exploring the look of the Los Muertos thugs.

BATTLE CHOREOGRAPHY

As the team created more shorts, they learned more about what art and
animation techniques worked best for Overwatch. There were no hard and

ALEJANDRA

One of the short's goals was to demonstrate how heroes inspire others. But for that to work, the team needed to show the world through the eyes of someone who *wasn't* a hero. Alejandra, who Soldier: 76 protects from the gang, was created to fill that role. While developing the story, the team imagined her as a tough girl who tried to live a good life in Dorado, the setting where the short takes place, but who also had one foot in the city's dark underbelly.

"The local thugs clearly know her, and she knows who they are," said Johnson. "She gets bullied, but she feels brave enough to fight back."

Based on these descriptions of Alejandra, artists fleshed out multiple versions of the character, trying to capture her bold personality and make her feel mature, despite her age. "She braids her hair to keep it out of her face. She's very practical, very pragmatic," said Johnson. "But she's still a kid, even though she's been forced to grow up maybe a little bit faster than she would've liked to."

THESE PAGES Concepts of Alejandra.

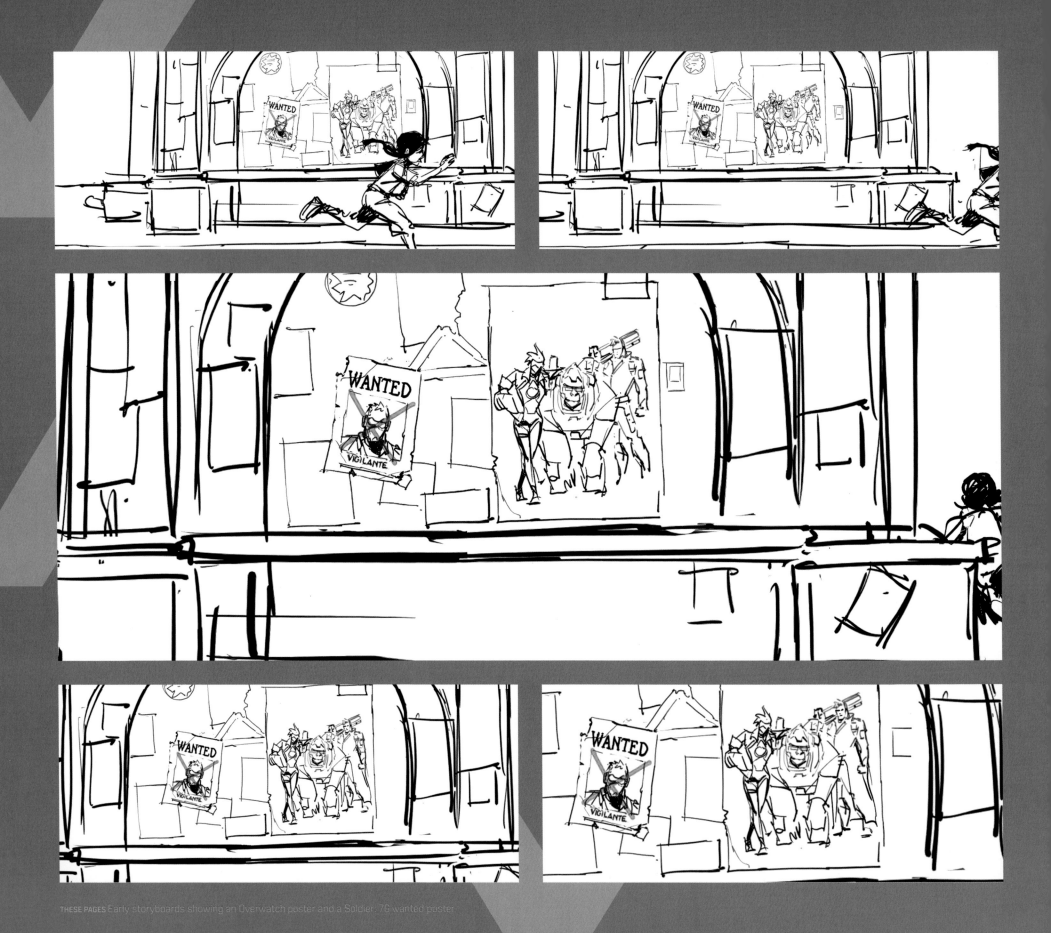

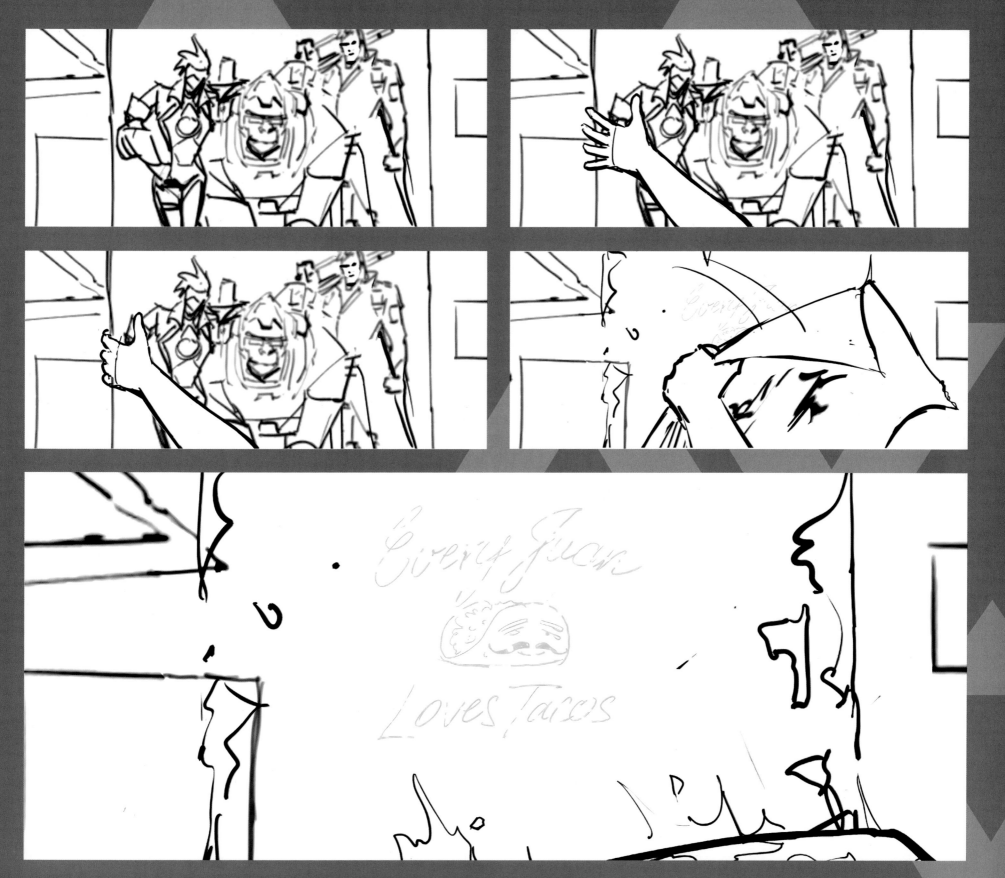

ARE YOU WITH US?

"SOMEONE HAS TO DO SOMETHING.
WE HAVE TO DO SOMETHING. WE
CAN MAKE A DIFFERENCE AGAIN.
THE WORLD NEEDS US NOW MORE
THAN EVER. ARE YOU WITH ME?"

—WINSTON

RIGHT Illustration of a scene from
London in "Are You With Us?"

"ARE YOU WITH US?" WAS A CLEAR DEPARTURE FROM THE FOUR

animated shorts that preceded it, in terms of length, scope, and purpose. The cinematic, crafted for the game's launch on May 24, 2016, would be the first thing anyone saw when they fired up *Overwatch*. It is a call to action for the heroes of Overwatch and for the players, as well as a refresher on the game's backstory.

"Are You With Us?" also tied directly into the "Recall" short. That cinematic shows Winston sending a message to the former agents of Overwatch but leaves viewers wondering, "What did he say?"

"Are You With Us?" was designed to answer that question, but it would have to do so in a limited timeframe. While most of the other shorts had run times of over six minutes, this one needed to be short and succinct, clocking in at a little over two minutes.

Another major difference from the previous cinematics was the restrictive setting. Filmed from the point of view of a webcam on Winston's desk in Watchpoint: Gibraltar, "Are You With Us?" uses a fixed camera position and has only one character. "It was a limitation," said director Aaron Chan. "But limitations are a great opportunity to find creative solutions that ultimately lead to a stronger piece."

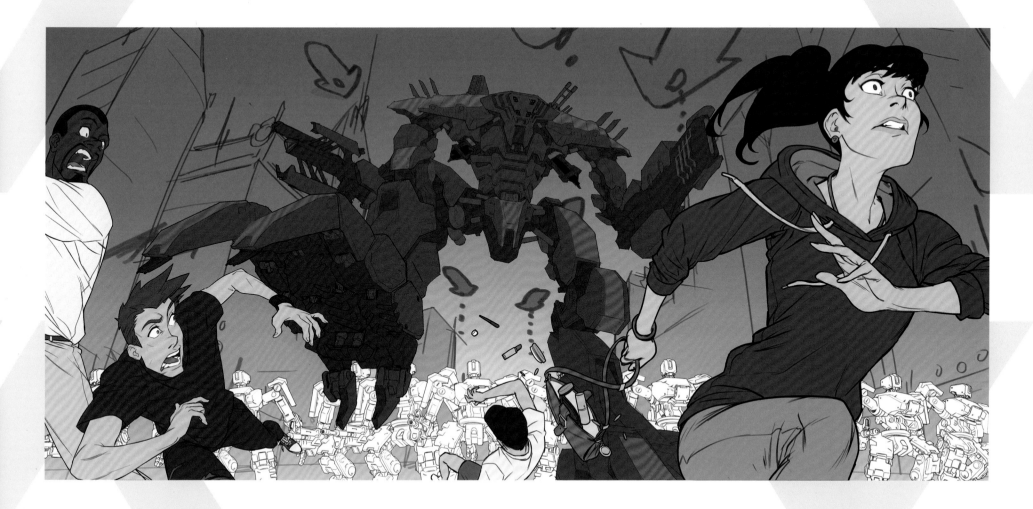

LIGHTING AND EMOTION

"Lighting and color were important aspects of telling the story," said Chan. "The art director, Stephan Belin, did a wonderful job of conveying the lighting idea—a day-to-night cycle. We wanted to light it really bright and friendly at the beginning to create a false sense of security."

The short starts in the morning with Winston's room bathed in warm light. But as he eagerly delivers his speech, things don't go as planned. He's nervous, and his words are too rehearsed. He keeps trying—and failing—to get the speech right as day turns to night, and he is eventually left alone in the dark.

"The lighting constantly reflected his emotional state," said Chan. "Winston is left at his lowest point alone in the dark, with only the cold-blue artificial light from his computer monitors illuminating him. The day-to-night cycle also subliminally communicates the time Winston has spent trying to get his speech right. This explains why he becomes so frustrated with himself."

At the end of the cinematic, Winston finally finds his voice and speaks from the heart. As he swipes through a series of 2D images showing the dire state of the world, he calls for the former agents of Overwatch to take a stand and do something.

"Because of the heartfelt turn at the end, we didn't want to leave Winston in the dark, both figuratively and literally," said Chan. The team found a lighting solution with the last image Winston shows onscreen—a fire raging in King's Row. "We used that as the practical reason to light the right side of Winston's face with a warm orange," said Chan. "

Which also dramatically contrasted with the cold blues in the dark room."

CREATIVE LIMITATIONS

One of the team's biggest goals was finding unique ways to frame shots, despite having only a single, fixed camera. Making the webcam accidentally tilt down when Winston started talking provided a bit of comedy and visual interest. The team also took artistic liberty to push in with the camera during the climactic moment of Winston's speech and even repositioned Winston within the frame periodically, giving the audience a glimpse into his emotional state.

"In the first two shots, he's not really framed up, so it's making things more casual and candid," said Chan. "It's like he's still figuring things out."

For the third shot, Winston is centered in frame, his shoulders squared so he's facing the camera directly. By design, this made him feel stiff, like he's now taking his speech too seriously.

The changes in Winston's positioning also give the impression that time is passing. But during his emotional moment in the middle of the cinematic, the camera stays on Winston. "Here, having no cuts in action allowed us to draw you in and feel Winston's moment," said Chan. "We wanted to focus on his performance."

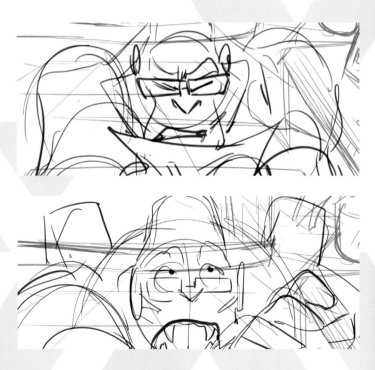

ABOVE & OPPOSITE Storyboards from the animated short.

RIGHT Early sketches of illustrations.

STORY WITHIN A STORY

▲ Including 2D illustrations in the cinematic was an inventive way to break from the fixed camera and feature other locations and characters. It was also an opportunity to introduce another storytelling layer to the piece, showing a brief history of the Overwatch organization's rise to glory. "By design, there is a simple story within the first sequence of 2D illustrations. The first image, with the omnics attacking the civilians, establishes the conflict. The second image depicts our heroes fighting back. The third is a lineup of our heroes being honored for their services. And the last image was meant to evoke a memory of a brighter time," said Chan. "Ending on this positive note contrasts with Winston alone in the present."

THESE PAGES In-progress illustrations depicting catastrophes in different parts of the world.

FOLLOWING PAGES Finished illustration from the cinematic.

The second sequence of 2D illustrations establishes the scale of devastation taking place around the world. These images cut rapidly from one to the next to build intensity, but the filmmakers needed to ensure the audience could still take them in at a glance. "We kept the focal point of each image at the center of the screen," said Chan. "The viewer can take everything in quickly without having to search the frame."

The global threat these illustrations portray motivates Winston to take action. They also give viewers a glimpse into the vast world of Overwatch—a world in dire need of help, where heroes like Winston are needed now more than ever. ▼

THIS PAGE Concept for a mech depicted in the animated short.

OPPOSITE In-progress versions of illustrations from the cinematic.

THE LAST BASTION

"IT WAS SO DIFFERENT FROM WHAT WE HAD DONE IN THE PAST, BUT EVERYONE WE PITCHED THE IDEA TO LOVED IT. WE KNEW WE HAD CAPTURED SOMETHING WITH UNIVERSAL APPEAL."

—JEFF CHAMBERLAIN, CODIRECTOR

RIGHT Concept painting of Bastion in the forest.

DECADES AGO, THE OMNIC CRISIS RAGED ACROSS THE WORLD.

Massive transport ships blotted out the sun, raining down drop pods filled with killing machines called Bastion units. Heavily armed and armored, they formed the bulk of the mechanized army that terrorized humanity. When the Omnic Crisis finally abated, almost all the Bastion units were destroyed or disassembled.

But there was at least one that was overlooked, and "The Last Bastion," released on August 18, 2016, tells its story.

The members of the story room knew early on that they wanted to develop a cinematic about the Bastion character, but they needed time to explore what that film could be. "There was one meeting we had where we were talking about one of the other animated shorts," said Jeff Chamberlain, codirector on the short alongside Ben Dai, who ultimately finished the piece. "We got to a point where we were happy with the idea, and we had about ten minutes left in the meeting. So we thought, 'Do we want to talk about this Bastion idea?'"

In those ten minutes, the story room brainstormed the basic moments of the short: Bastion waking up in a lush forest, exploring its beauty, and then having to choose between staying there or following its violent programming to wage war on humanity.

"I happened to have to go home right after that to watch my kid," said Chamberlain. Since it was still early in the day, he strapped his child into a stroller and went for a walk. But what was meant to be a thirty-minute stroll turned into an hours-long journey of discovery. "I was just lost in my head about this Bastion piece."

Chamberlain later wrote down his thoughts, creating a shot-by-shot breakdown of the short. Inspired by this initial outline and ideas from the earlier meeting, the members of the story room agreed to move forward and continue fleshing out the piece.

The story was unlike anything that Blizzard had told in the past. "It was interesting in that the main character doesn't talk or have typical facial expressions," said Dai. "It relied on the most rudimentary form of acting: using your body language to talk."

The central idea of a robot exploring a forest also called for slower, more reflective pacing and editing than the earlier cinematics, making "The Last Bastion" a step into the unknown, much like the first Overwatch cinematics had been. But the team felt they had a strong idea they could bring to life via the different stages of production.

THIS PAGE Concepts of Bastion and the forest environment.

FALLING IN LOVE WITH THE FOREST

The short takes place in the heart of Germany's Black Forest, an inspiring real-world location that hadn't yet been developed in the game, giving the team an opportunity to create beautiful visuals from scratch. But the setting needed to be more than just a pretty backdrop. "I remember telling the group, 'We need to understand why Bastion falls in love with the forest,'" said Chamberlain. "We need to fall in love with it too."

The whole story hinged on infusing the forest with a sense of wonder. Otherwise, Bastion's ultimate choice—to side with peaceful nature over his violent programming—wouldn't work.

Creating the forest began with blue-sky concepting. Artists were given a basic pitch about the story and then let loose to paint Bastion, the forest and its creatures, or anything else they thought would be relevant. But no matter what they illustrated, they were encouraged to capture that sense of wonder that was so critical to the piece.

Clear visibility, shafts of light coming through the trees, and dew glistening on leaves were just some of the visuals the team experimented with to find the right tone and feeling. "The main thing you want to think about is the experience of the viewer and what elements people really like. It's supposed to feel not just magical but safe and pleasant," said senior artist Laurel Austin.

The blue-sky period produced dozens of stunning paintings, some of which went on to become shots in the final version of the short. But even the ones that got cut served an important purpose: they helped the team discover what a forest would look like in the world of Overwatch.

LEFT Paintings exploring the changing of the seasons.

TOP RIGHT Concept of the forest environment.

THIS PAGE Concepts from an early version of the story, which included a human girl.

OPPOSITE Concept of Bastion exploring the forest.

EARLY STORY DEVELOPMENT

Ideas often change during the early visual and story development of the shorts. In an early script, a father and daughter were going to discover the dormant Bastion during a hike through the forest. The purpose of this brief encounter was to illustrate how dangerous the robot was: after finding Bastion, the father would warn his daughter that it was a deadly war machine and then whisk her away to safety. This idea was put aside to focus all the attention on Bastion and its feathered friend, the yellow bird Ganymede.

Another idea that was explored early on was using time-lapse to convey duration. During the opening shot of the piece, the camera would push through the forest as the seasons changed, eventually locating Bastion. "The idea was that the robot has been there for decades," said Chamberlain. "By the end, you realize you're seeing this robot, and it's overgrown."

The team later decided they didn't need to change the seasons. Finding Bastion in the woods, covered in plants, was enough to show in a single image that the robot hadn't moved in years.

During the blue-sky period, artists researched plants and animals native to the Black Forest region. Different versions of Ganymede were also created, such as this image created by senior artist Laurel Austin, which was based on the citrine wagtail.

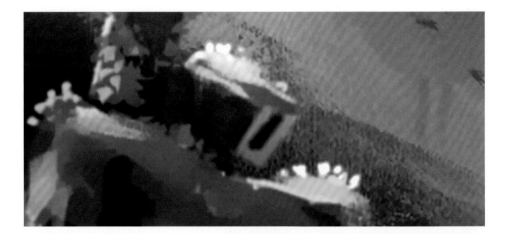

LEFT Concepts of Ganymede.

ABOVE & OPPOSITE Concepts of Bastion and an early version of Ganymede.

FAKING FEATHERS

▲ The team went through several tests to get Ganymede right. Creating a bird in the Overwatch world wasn't something they had done before. How would they create feathers? And how should the feathers look and move to fit with the Overwatch aesthetic?

"The funny thing about the bird is that there's not a single feather on it," said CG supervisor Shimon Cohen. "It's almost all fur."

But even the fur presented challenges. After rendering Ganymede in test shots, something wasn't quite right. "It looked very harsh," said Cohen. "Too much like hair."

The solution lay in manipulating light and shadow. The team adjusted Ganymede's fur so that it would absorb all light penetrating it, which made the bird look bright, soft, and fluffy.

For Ganymede's wings and tail, feathers were modeled as solid objects, rather than real feathers, which are composed of thousands of individual barbs. ▼

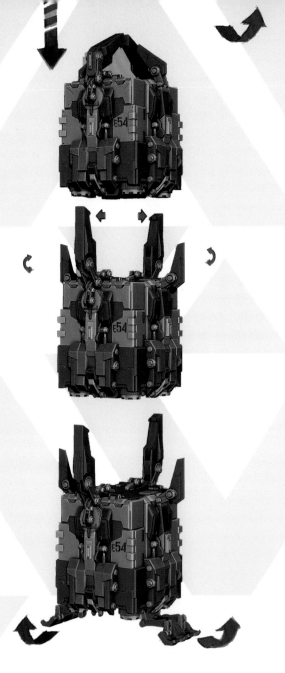

THE DUD

▲ "The Last Bastion" was a story with no dialogue; everything was told visually. This challenged the team to find creative ways to explain Bastion's backstory. For one, why was he in the forest?

"My thinking in development was that Bastion is basically the dud," said Chamberlain. "His drop pod landed, but never opened."

Artists designed a drop pod, which was subtly placed under Bastion at the beginning of the piece to hint at his origins. The idea that the robot fell from the sky was later reinforced in the flashback, when massive omnic ships launch hundreds of pods into the forest. ▼

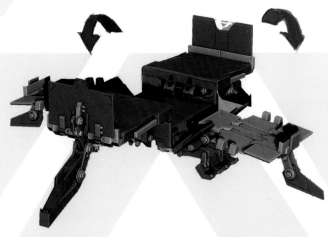

OPPOSITE Explorations of Bastion's drop pod.

THIS PAGE Concepts exploring the amount of overgrowth covering Bastion.

BALANCING DETAIL

A dense forest filled with light, color, trees, and animals is a feast for the eyes, but all those elements can potentially war for the audience's attention. "We had to plan the lighting carefully and design the plant life with strong silhouettes to keep it all readable and not overly distracting," said art director Mathias Verhasselt.

Although simplifying detail was a major goal, the team still wanted to deliver a sense of scale, depth, and richness. "There's no real recipe for that, but it was something we tried to get right very early on, and that's why I painted the tree next to Bastion," said visual development artist Stephan Belin. "It served two purposes: convey a sense of scale and fantasy but also simplify the composition so that we wouldn't have to fight the noise of trees overlapping everywhere."

To craft the illusion of depth, the artists used traditional 2D animation layout techniques. "The trees that are further away from the camera have simpler values. Starting from the back, it's just one color. And then it's a breakout of maybe two or three values. Then as you get closer to the camera, it becomes a little bit more detailed," said Belin.

It was relatively simple for artists to create this effect in 2D paintings but mimicking it in 3D required a lot of experimentation and fine-tuning. "The rendering software would want to light every single little leaf," said Belin. "It was a lot of work to try and simplify the surface of things as much as possible to avoid any noise that would affect the readability of the shot."

TOP RIGHT Scale study depicting Bastion next to a tree from the forest.

MIDDLE & RIGHT Black-and-white concepts from the blue-sky period.

OPPOSITE Color concepts of Bastion and different forest locations.

BRINGING THE FOREST TO LIFE

Previous cinematics had taken place in cities, towns, the corridors of lunar colonies, and other locations built out of inanimate materials. They were static locations that never moved unless acted upon by the characters. But the forest in "The Last Bastion" was just the opposite. The environment itself was a living, breathing ecosystem.

This prompted an initial debate among the filmmakers about whether to animate parts of the forest, but everyone ultimately realized that some amount of animation, even as subtle as the swaying of trees in the background, was important. "Without movement, it seemed like a dead place," said Dai. "With just a little bit of movement, everything came to life."

OPPOSITE, TOP Exploration of scale and stylization for the trees.

OPPOSITE, BOTTOM Paint-over image conveying light and color.

THIS PAGE Color keys for "The Last Bastion."

SYMBOLIC COLORS

Color was used symbolically throughout the story to emphasize Bastion's changing emotional state. For instance, when the character became frightened by the sound of a woodpecker and mowed down part of the forest with a Gatling gun, the team desaturated the normally vibrant surroundings. The team also used the vertical light on Bastion's head to illustrate the internal struggle between peace and war that grips the robot. As Bastion interacts with the forest, the light is blue, but after the character experiences a violent flashback, it flickers and switches to red.

The flashback itself led to the film's most drastic shift in color. Near the end of the piece, Bastion discovers a field of broken robots—an overgrown battlefield from years ago. When Bastion interfaces with one of them, the encounter triggers a terrifying change of scenery.

One moment, the character is standing in an open field of bright-green grass under a deep-blue sky. The next, Bastion is trapped in a flashback of the conflict, the scorched earth painted in browns and blacks, the dark sky lit in fiery reds, oranges, and yellows. "We knew we wanted to have this very distinct change of look," said Chamberlain. "We wanted to go from heaven to hell."

OPPOSITE Concepts exploring different settings and ideas for shots.

THIS PAGE Paintings of Bastion's battle flashback.

ANIMATING BASTION

▲ Unlike the other animated shorts, the main character of "The Last Bastion" doesn't speak or have any traditional facial features to express emotion. It fell to the animators to convey what Bastion was feeling through its body language.

"I really wanted the character to feel like an old clunky car. When Bastion is in happy mode, the robot is always shaking. It's always looking around, trying to soak up all the information. The way Bastion acts is like a child," said Dai. "And then when the robot's in war mode, it becomes very static and still. Everything it does is very deliberate. Bastion's all business." ▼

THESE PAGES Early storyboards for the animated short.

FOLLOWING PAGES Concept of Bastion at the edge of the forest.

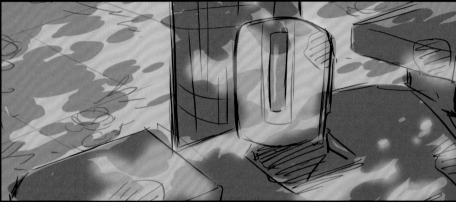

INFILTRATION

"I'LL BE IN TOUCH. BOOP."

—SOMBRA

ON NOVEMBER 4, 2016, THOUSANDS OF PEOPLE DESCENDED ON the Anaheim Convention Center to attend another BlizzCon—the first since the official release of *Overwatch* on May 24, 2016. Two years had passed since *Overwatch*'s announcement trailer premiered at the same venue, and the stage was set for the reveal of a new cinematic. But this time, things would play out differently.

During the opening ceremony, Blizzard Entertainment's president, Mike Morhaime, took the stage and introduced a video looking back on the worldwide launch of *Overwatch* five months prior. Partway through the retrospective film, something happened. The audio and visuals stuttered and glitched out as if someone had hacked the presentation.

That someone was Sombra, *Overwatch*'s newest character. As the video cut out, the "Infiltration" animated short began, introducing the world to the brilliant hacker in all her snarky glory.

"Infiltration" was the first cinematic to coincide with the release of a completely new Overwatch character. After the animated short was shown at BlizzCon, attendees were able to play Sombra in demo builds of the game. Developing the in-game and cinematic versions of Sombra in parallel so they would feel cohesive had been a new and immense challenge, requiring constant iteration on art and story.

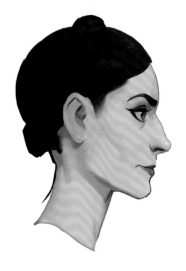

THIS PAGE Concepts exploring the look of Katya Volskaya.

OPPOSITE Early sketches for the photographs of Katya's daughter and the secretive deal Katya makes with an omnic.

KATYA VOLSKAYA

For the team to show Sombra's strength and resourcefulness, they needed an equally formidable character for her to oppose. That role was filled by Katya Volskaya, the powerful and controlled CEO of Volskaya Industries.

Katya's design began with a portrait that had been created for the Volskaya Industries game map. Visual development principal artist Laurel Austin used this image as a blueprint to explore the CEO's physical appearance. The goal was to convey her professionalism and wealth through every detail—from her sleek, tight-to-the-head chignon French hairstyle to her tailored wardrobe.

"She's an 'everything in its place' kind of character," said Austin. "She has this wool blazer on top, and underneath, she has a ribbed sweater, and underneath that, she has a smoother fabric. Layering of texture adds to the feeling of wealth and quality."

But there is more to Katya than her outward appearance. She is also a loving mother, which is revealed through a photograph in her office. Many of the concepts created for the portrait contained three key elements: Katya, her daughter, and a mech symbolizing Volskaya Industries. "I wanted to explore their relationship," said visual development artist Will Murai. "I also wanted to convey the idea that, for Katya, her daughter isn't only the most valuable thing in the world but also that she will inherit her mother's empire one day."

The final concept chosen for the short didn't feature Katya, but her daughter's expression and the candidness of the moment spoke volumes about the relationship between the two characters. "It showed a child looking back at the mom she loves," said director Doug Gregory. "When Katya looks at it, she sees a reflection of herself. Maybe this is the childhood she wanted but never had, and now she can give it to her child."

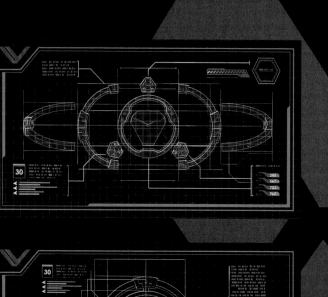

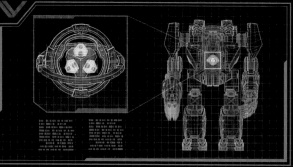

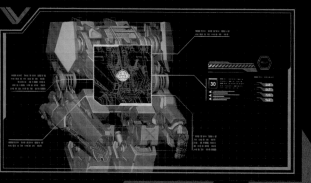

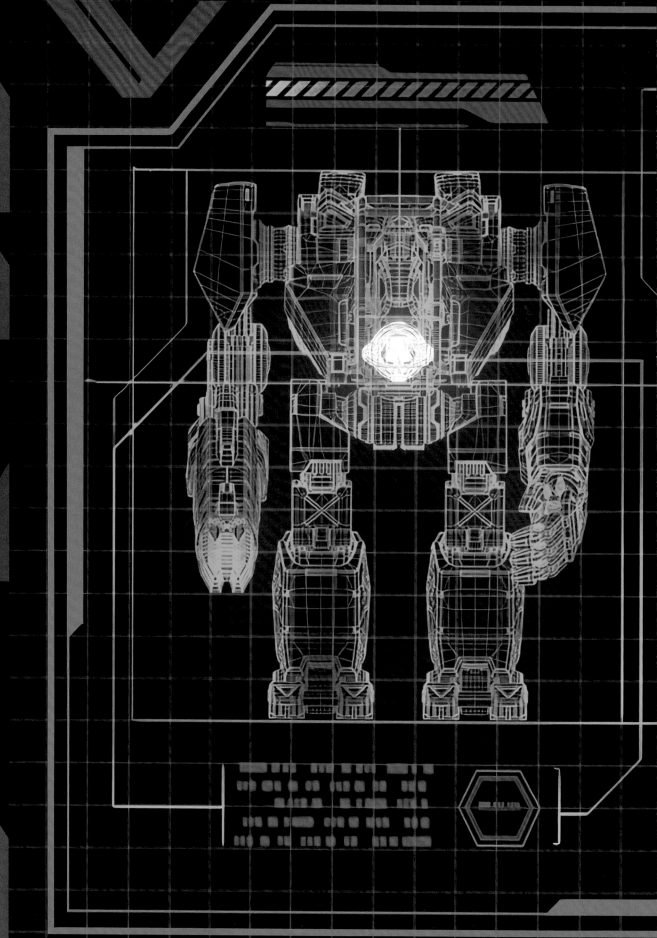

THESE PAGES Illustrations of schematics that
...atya receives from an omnic.

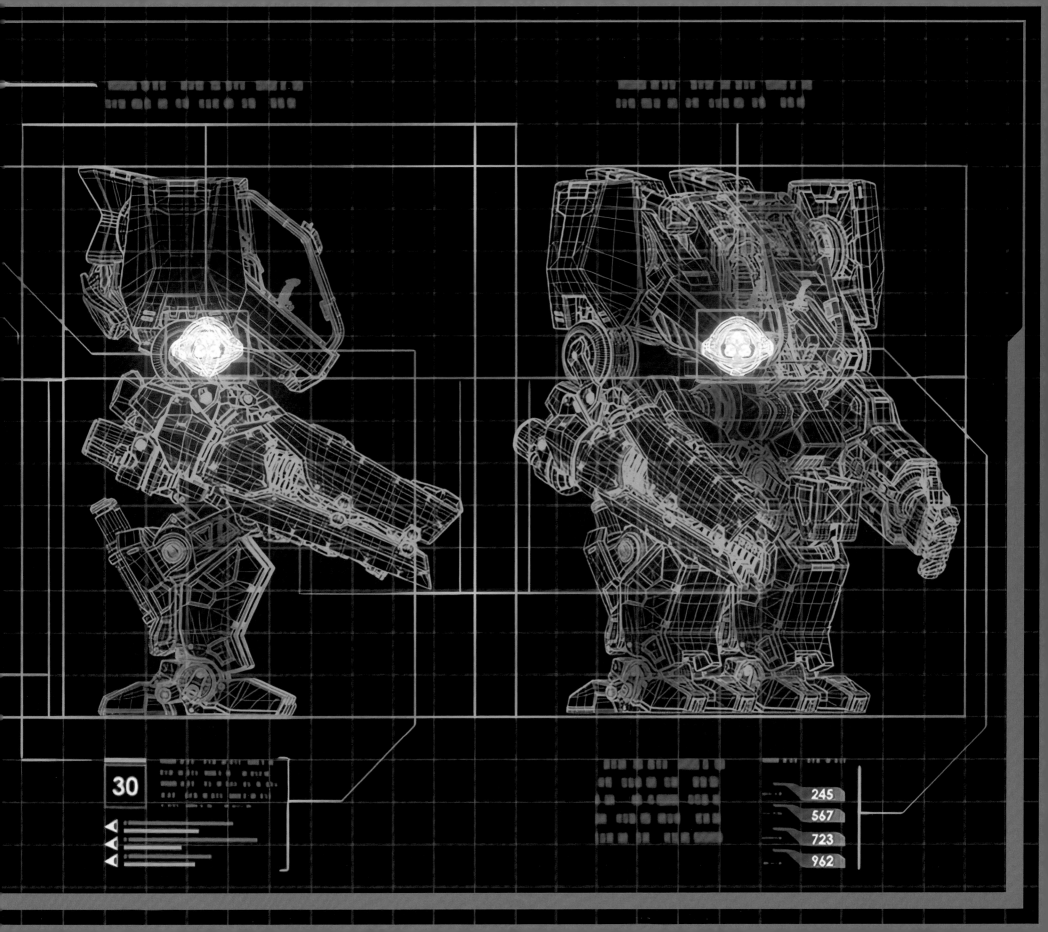

ADAPTING TO ABILITIES

Unlike most of the previous cinematics, "Infiltration" revolves around the villains of Talon, a shadowy organization opposed to Overwatch and its altruistic goals. "There was a need to see Talon in operation," said senior writer Andrew Robinson, who wrote the piece. "Who are they? How do they work together? Can they have a little fun?"

"Infiltration" follows Sombra and her fellow Talon agents Reaper and Widowmaker as they run a covert operation in Volskaya Industries, a fortresslike mech factory in Russia. Their mission to assassinate the company's CEO, Katya, soon goes awry when the facility's alarm system is tripped. Only later is it revealed that Sombra set off the security system. Her goals are not the same as Talon's: instead of killing Katya, Sombra plans on keeping her alive to use as a powerful ally in the future.

When production on "Infiltration" began, Sombra's in-game abilities were still under development. Based on her early concept art, the team tried to find a visual language for her powers that would work well in the cinematic world but also stay true to the essence of what had been made for the game thus far.

ABOVE Concept of Volskaya Industries.

RIGHT & OPPOSITE Storyboards for the animated short.

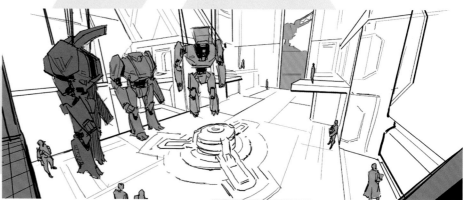

One area that needed exploration was Sombra's hacking abilities. Visual development artist Jungah Lee created a design inspired by circuit boards and the character's bright-purple color palette. This effect appears in the short when Sombra hacks the arm of a colossal mech, using it as a shield to protect her from enemy gunfire as it lifts her closer to Katya.

Along with the visuals, fundamental elements of the story also underwent changes during production. In one early version, the filmmakers planned for Sombra to stay in a control room for the entire short, hacking parts of the Volskaya factory from afar. This would have allowed the team to showcase the character in a way that wouldn't contradict the final version of her in-game abilities. "Visually, it just wasn't very satisfying if Sombra is in a room the whole time," said Robinson. "We adjusted the story to showcase her abilities and make her more dynamic."

As Sombra's final powers were fleshed out, the team planned for the hacker to break into Katya's highly secure office, only to discover that it's a trap. The CEO—safely off-site—would appear on monitors in the room, and the two powerful characters would engage in a duel of words.

"We could never quite crack that version," said Gregory. "And I think what it came down to was there was no threat or urgency with both characters in separate locations. The thing to do would be to put them both in the room together. That's where the drama would happen. That's ultimately what we did."

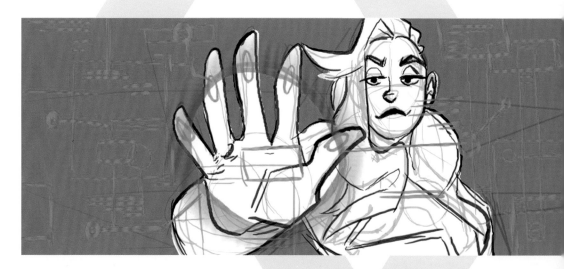

CONTROL AND DOMINANCE

Control and dominance are important themes in "Infiltration," and the team harnessed the dramatic power of lighting to illustrate them throughout the short, consciously breaking away from earlier conventions to craft a darker setting that featured deeper shadows. This design choice played into the fantasy of a clandestine Talon mission, but it also made Volskaya Industries feel immense and formidable. Mechs loom like monstrous guardians standing vigil over Katya and her people in the facility's dark interior.

"A lot of small lights in a bigger space emphasized the scale we wanted, which was to contrast what was happening in the story. Sombra is this really tiny thing that's running through this gigantic space, and all of it is meant to celebrate Katya," said Gregory. "We also knew that as soon as the alarm goes off, the darker everything was, the more the red emergency lights would really pop, and so would any of our other spotlights."

THESE PAGES Concept art exploring color schemes and different moments from the animated short.

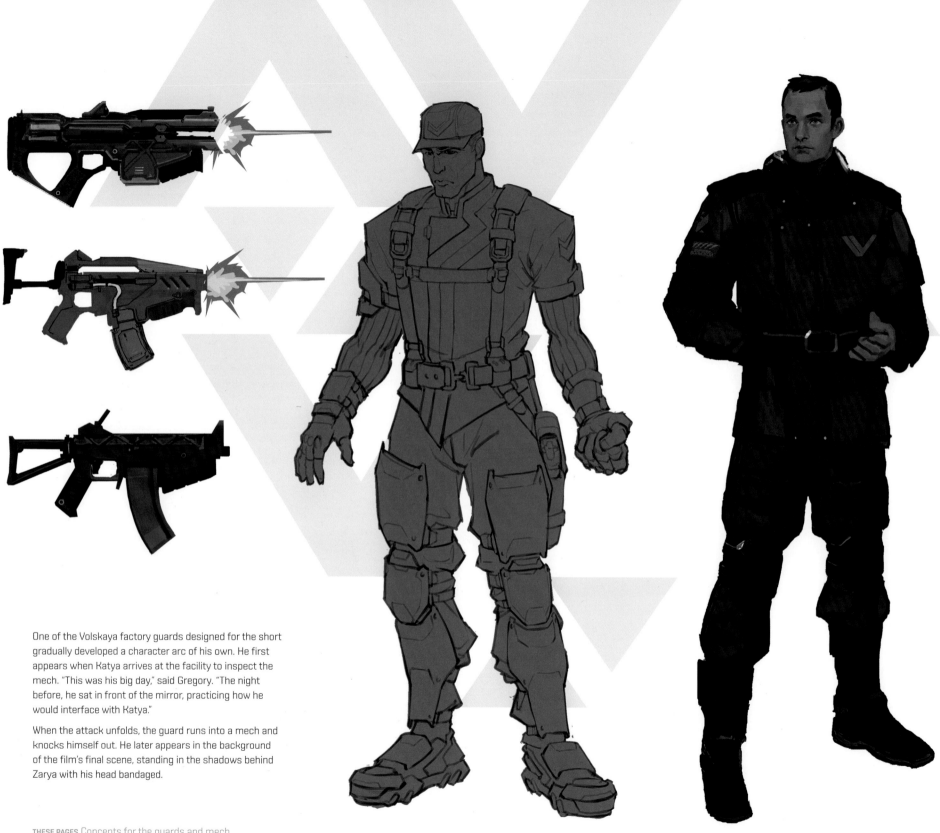

One of the Volskaya factory guards designed for the short gradually developed a character arc of his own. He first appears when Katya arrives at the facility to inspect the mech. "This was his big day," said Gregory. "The night before, he sat in front of the mirror, practicing how he would interface with Katya."

When the attack unfolds, the guard runs into a mech and knocks himself out. He later appears in the background of the film's final scene, standing in the shadows behind Zarya with his head bandaged.

THESE PAGES Concepts for the guards and mech pilots who work for Volskaya Industries.

Based on Russia's history of conflict with omnics, the artists wanted to telegraph that the machines were not automated or sentient but controlled by humans. Making the pilot's suit bright red drew the viewer's eye to the character and showed that a person was the heart of the mech.

open

LEFT, ABOVE, RIGHT & OPPOSITE Concepts of the mech pilot.

BELOW Concepts exploring different versions of the mech.

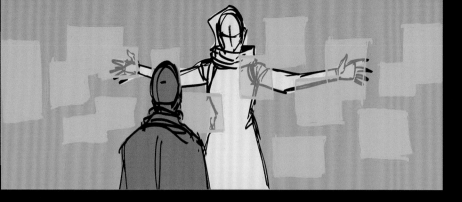

BALANCE OF POWER

At the climax of "Infiltration," Sombra corners Katya in the CEO's fortified office. This face-to-face confrontation was the dramatic heart of the short, and the filmmakers engineered every element of the scene to show that both characters were powerful in their own way. Artists designed the office so that Sombra and Katya both dominated their own corner of the room. On Katya's side of the office, warm lights spill across a glorious mural of Russian pride—a giant relief showing the country's soldiers bravely fighting against enemy omnics.

"We wanted that to give you a sense of, 'Oh. Katya is safe now. She's in the warmth of her office, of her reputation. She's got everything around her that she needs,'" said Gregory. "But that's just one corner of the room, and the rest of the lighting is all this cool color, which fits Sombra."

As the scene plays out, Sombra reveals her intentions. She blackmails Katya with photographs that prove the CEO has been secretly acquiring technology from omnics. In Russia, where antiomnic sentiment runs high, such images would likely destroy Katya's career and reputation if they ever went public. The team shot and

THIS PAGE Storyboards for the animated short.

OPPOSITE Early concepts exploring the lighting and color of Katya's office.

FOLLOWING PAGES Concept of Zarya greeting Katya after her encounter with Sombra.

edited the conversation so that the two characters are framed by their respective parts of the room, creating a constantly shifting balance of power.

The two powerful women agree to a truce, and Sombra disappears just as Katya's guards enter the room. The final scene of the film takes place in Katya's office sometime after her encounter with Sombra. Gone are the shadows and cold colors that dominated parts of it when the hacker was present. Bright warm light floods the room through a giant window. Katya, standing by the glass, gazes out at a futuristic city in the distance as a new character enters the frame, eager to help—the Russian Overwatch hero Zarya.

"At least for me, psychologically, what she has to be going through in her head is, 'I have all the light in the world I need here, but I'm in a room that can turn into a box very quickly, and all the light can be sucked out. Somebody just did that to me, and it made me feel foolish and insecure. Now I'm going to call on the help of the national treasure that is Zarya,'" said Gregory.

ORIGIN STORIES

THREE
▼

THE 3D ANNOUNCEMENT TRAILER AND ANIMATED SHORTS WEREN'T THE ONLY VISUAL STORYTELLING TOOLS USED TO EXPLORE OVERWATCH'S WORLD AND CHARACTERS. Alongside the game's reveal at BlizzCon 2014, Blizzard released the first in a series of 2D animations that would later be called "origin stories."

Whereas the 3D shorts were snapshots of the characters at specific moments in time, the 2D origins focus more on where the heroes come from, presenting a broader view of their lives, personalities, and their place in the world. Rarely more than two minutes long, these pieces are designed to work in harmony with the 3D cinematics to enrich the world of Overwatch.

"We wanted to show that there was more to these heroes than, 'Hey, here's a cool class you can play,'" said lead character artist Arnold Tsang, who created the art for many of the early origin pieces. "We wanted to make sure that they stood out as individuals with their own interesting backstories."

LEFT Overwatch hero illustration revealed in the announcement trailer.

The origins don't have the complex models, intricate special effects, and meticulous lighting setups of the 3D animated shorts. Rather, they use a flexible form of 2.5D visual storytelling called "motion-story," a medium that enhances 2D illustrations with limited movement and special effects. This approach requires less time and resources than 3D cinematics and gives the creators a wide berth to explore. For example, in the animated shorts, any new location requires an entire 3D set. But the origins can switch between drastically different settings in the same story simply by using illustrations.

On average, each origin comprises around seven illustrations, which tell a story through still images much like comics or storyboards. The art developed for these pieces expresses Overwatch's distinct style and is reminiscent of the game's concept art. "When you announce a new universe and art style, you want things to be as consistent and coherent as possible," said Tsang. "I think that played a huge role in why we made the origins this way. It definitely helped cement Overwatch's art style."

THIS PAGE Sketches from the Solider: 76, Junkers, and Ana origin stories.

OPPOSITE Color illustration from the Junkers origin story.

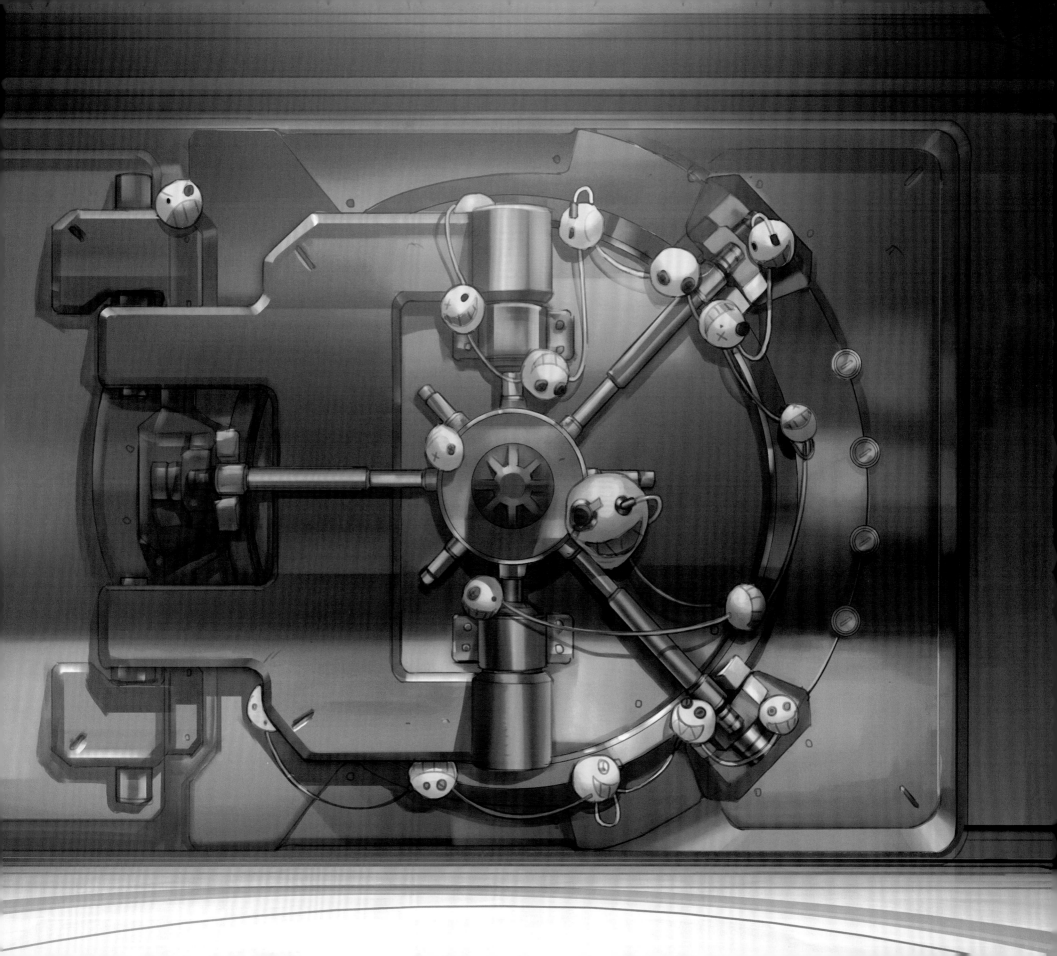

TRACER

"WHEN WE STARTED, WE DIDN'T THINK WE WERE GOING TO DO A SERIES. WE HOPED THAT IF WE TOLD YOU TRACER'S HISTORY, YOU WOULD REALIZE THAT EVERY OTHER CHARACTER ALSO HAD A SIMILARLY FLESHED OUT BACKSTORY."

—MICHAEL CHU, LEAD WRITER

IN THE MONTHS LEADING UP TO BLIZZCON 2014, MEMBERS of the team met to brainstorm how they could explore the depth of the game's characters. Designer Jeremy Craig asked a question that gave birth to the origin pieces: What if the team created a series of images showing different moments in a character's backstory?

There wasn't enough time to explore every character, but creating a window into one of them was possible. After looking through the lineup of initial heroes, the team focused on Tracer. She was slated to be featured heavily in the announcement trailer, making her one of the more recognizable characters. Her backstory also spoke to the level of technology in Overwatch's science-fiction universe. While test-piloting an experimental teleporting fighter plane called the Slipstream, Tracer suffered an accident that desynchronized her from the flow of time. Winston eventually created a special device—the chronal accelerator—that anchored Tracer back in the present and gave her the ability to manipulate where she is in time.

Lead character artist Arnold Tsang immediately began sketching out different moments for Tracer's backstory while lead writer Michael Chu created dialogue to accompany each image. From a visual standpoint, the approach was something between an illustration and what storyboard artists would typically make during production for a 3D animation.

"In a storyboard, you have more shots and animation to tell your story," said Tsang. "Here, you're picking specific shots to say just one thing. There might be a little movement, but there's not much. It's somewhere in between animation and illustration."

RIGHT Line art of Tracer in the experimental Slipstream aircraft.

SLIPSTREAM

The deadline for the Tracer origin story was short; BlizzCon was fast approaching. To save time, the images were painted in blue monotone instead of full color. But this limitation worked well for the piece. The muted colors made the cinematic feel like a flashback, a style that would influence future origins.

Tracer's story also cemented the use of first-person voice-over in the origin pieces. The team had decided on having the character narrate her own backstory early in the project, but the true potential of that decision didn't become clear until they watched an edit with sound cut in.

"I thought it was really interesting to hear the characters talk about themselves in their own voice," said Chu. "It helps to narrow the gap between your understanding of the character and who they are."

Having Tracer tell her own story brought an emotional richness to the piece that wouldn't have been possible with a nameless, omniscient narrator. Tracer's voice-over helped audiences—and even the team working on Overwatch and its cinematics—connect with the character like never before.

The first round of sketches for Tracer's origin depicted her in a hospital room, but this was changed to a special high-tech chamber. The adjustment showed that the character's condition wasn't medical in nature; it was a technical glitch that could only be fixed with technology.

OPPOSITE & BELOW Sketches and final art from the origin piece.

RIGHT & FOLLOWING PAGES In-progress illustrations of the hospital room, which appeared in an early version of the cinematic.

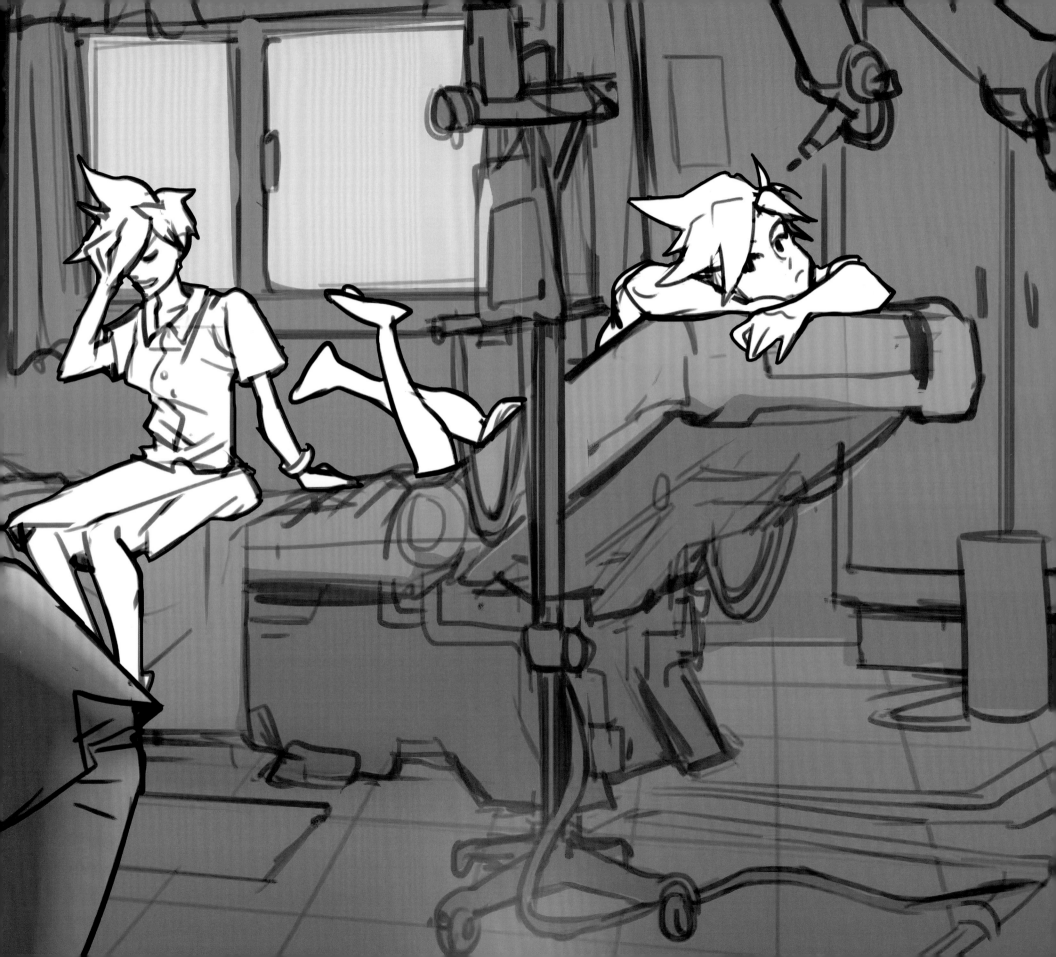

LEFT Final illustration of Tracer as a test pilot.

SOLDIER: 76

"EACH PIECE WAS NOT ONLY SUPPOSED TO EXPLORE ONE OF THE HEROES BUT ALSO REALLY ILLUSTRATE PART OF OVERWATCH GEOGRAPHICALLY AND THEMATICALLY."

—MICHAEL CHU, LEAD WRITER

SOLDIER: 76'S ORIGIN—RELEASED ON JULY 7, 2015—WAS heavily influenced by the style of Tracer's piece. Like hers, Soldier: 76's story is conveyed in flashbacks with earthy sepia tones instead of full color, giving it an air of history and somber nostalgia. Achieving this effect was especially important for Soldier: 76 since he was a central figure in Overwatch's backstory.

"We wanted to tell not just Soldier: 76's story but some of Overwatch's story as well," said lead character artist Arnold Tsang, who created the art for the piece. "How Overwatch fell. The state of the world. Things like that."

After rough sketches and dialogue were created for the origin story, the pieces were combined into an early edit featuring camera moves and temporary voice-over. This animatic gave a sense of pacing and tone, as well as the ways the camera could zoom and pan across the images. From there, the creators fine-tuned the writing, art, and other elements before finishing the illustrations and recording final dialogue. As future origins started using more complex motion-story techniques, planning out timing and camera movements in this way would become even more important.

RIGHT In-progress illustration for the final shot of Soldier: 76's origin piece.

Soldier: 76's origin piece featured a photograph of some of Overwatch's original members: Reinhardt Wilhelm, Ana Amari, Gabriel Reyes, Torbjörn Lindholm, and Jack Morrison (who would become Soldier: 76). One of the challenges of creating this image was deciding what heroes should be present at that point in history, when Overwatch had just formed. Originally, Mercy appeared alongside the other characters, but the team decided that she wouldn't have been part of the group yet.

This depiction of early Overwatch was also the first time the team revealed the sniper Ana to the world.

TOP Early sketch including Mercy instead of Ana.

RIGHT & OPPOSITE, TOP In-progress illustrations for the Soldier: 76 origin story.

THE CINEMATIC ART OF OVERWATCH

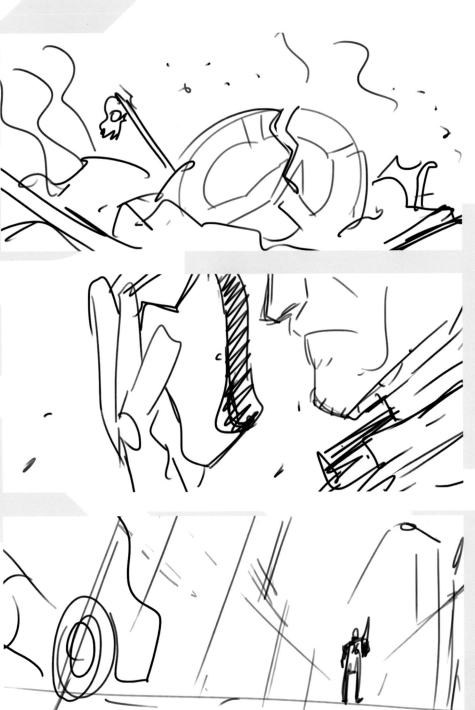

THESE PAGES Sketches from the early stages of production.

FOLLOWING PAGES In-progress version of the origin story's final illustration.

A MOMENT IN CRIME SPECIAL REPORT: "THE JUNKERS"

"VERY EARLY ON, WE DECIDED, 'LET'S NOT GET INTO A RUT.' SO FOR THE JUNKRAT AND ROADHOG PIECE, WE DID SOMETHING COMPLETELY DIFFERENT."

—MICHAEL CHU, LEAD WRITER

THE EXPLOSIVES-LOVING MANIAC, JUNKRAT, AND HIS MENACING partner in crime, Roadhog, are two of Overwatch's most distinct characters. When they were created, they expanded the possibilities for the game's tone, art style, and storytelling. Unlike Tracer and Soldier: 76, Junkrat and Roadhog were never members of Overwatch, so their backstories didn't need to be tied so closely to the game's core narrative. Making an origin story for them seemed like the perfect opportunity to try something new.

"This was much different in tone from Soldier: 76, which was a somber flashback where you're watching these old events happen," said lead character artist Arnold Tsang, who created the illustrations for "A Moment in Crime Special Report: 'The Junkers'" with help from artist Justin Thavirat, then the senior art department supervisor for Creative Development.

Released on September 21, 2015, Junkrat and Roadhog's origin story presented the characters through a tongue-in-cheek TV show called "A Moment in Crime," which chronicled their heists and hijinks around the world.

RIGHT Line art of Junkrat and Roadhog terrorizing a Japanese arcade.

FOLLOWING PAGES Illustration of Roadhog from the origin piece.

Full color was used instead of the monochromatic style of the previous origins. The team also brought more complex motion-story techniques to the piece, such as the shot where Roadhog's hook yanks off the back of an ice cream truck, sending waffle cones tumbling through the air. This was achieved by breaking apart the illustration into independent elements—such as the hook, door, and waffle cones—and then animating these pieces separately to create a dynamic parallax effect.

THIS PAGE Early illustrations showing Junkrat's and Roadhog's crime spree.

OPPOSITE, TOP LEFT, TOP RIGHT, BOTTOM LEFT & BOTTOM RIGHT In-progress art of Junkrat's and Roadhog's mug shots.

OPPOSITE, BOTTOM MIDDLE Line art for the piece, which was slightly altered for the final version.

COMPOSITION FIRST

▲ Creating the illustrations began with composition as it was important to craft dynamic, action-packed images of Junkrat and Roadhog in the middle of their crime spree. *Where* those crimes were taking place was secondary, at least to begin. Many of the locations used in the first sketches were later swapped out for different places. For example, the final illustration of Junkrat and Roadhog roaring through the streets of London was originally staged in the Australian outback. "We decided on the setting later," said Tsang. "But elements in the illustrations remained the same, like the car next to the bus in the London scene." ▼

RIGHT Final illustration of Junkrat and Roadhog in London.

FOLLOWING PAGES Final illustration of Junkrat and Roadhog terrorizing a Japanese arcade.

ANA

"WHAT'S SO EXCITING ABOUT WORKING ON A PIECE THAT FOCUSES ON A CHARACTER IS THE OPPORTUNITY TO QUICKLY ESTABLISH A REASON TO CARE ABOUT THEM."

—TIMOTHY LOUGHRAN, SENIOR PRODUCER

ANA'S ORIGIN STORY, WHICH CAME OUT JULY 12, 2016, drew inspiration from the previous pieces in different ways. The gifted sniper was one of Overwatch's original members, a hero from a bygone era. To give her backstory the gravity it needed, the team returned to the sepia tones used in Soldier: 76's cinematic, where she had first been introduced. What made Ana's origin story different was the type of story it told.

Soldier: 76's piece had been far-reaching, as much about Overwatch's history as his own. Ana's origin was more personal. The voice-over was presented as a heartfelt message from the character to her daughter, another hero in the game named Pharah. In the narration, Ana explains her worldview, the difficult choices she had to make during her career in Overwatch, and the reasons why she eventually went into hiding—even from her own daughter.

The illustrations in the piece complement the dialogue, showing moments of Pharah being raised by Ana and explaining the circumstances behind her disappearance. Building off the work they had done for Junkrat and Roadhog's origin, the team brought more movement, special effects, and other motion-story elements to the piece.

RIGHT Sketch of Ana, young Pharah, and members of Overwatch. Torbjörn was later changed to depict him with a cybernetic arm.

THE CINEMATIC ART OF OVERWATCH

THE QUEST FOR CONTINUITY

▲ Ana's origin features a photograph of the character and her daughter surrounded by Reinhardt, Jack Morrison, Gabriel Reyes, Mercy, McCree, and other iconic Overwatch heroes. The image is important because it establishes how much these people mean to Ana, but it also presented challenges.

Showing characters from earlier periods of history always requires careful attention to detail, mainly because the heroes change over time. Some simply grow older, but others undergo more drastic changes. For example, the team originally created the photograph showing Torbjörn with his flesh-and-blood arm, only to realize that by that point in the Overwatch story, he would have lost his limb and replaced it with a cybernetic one. "It's tough because you have to get everything right," said lead character artist Arnold Tsang, who illustrated the origin story with concept artists Ben Zhang, John Polidora, and David Kang. "It's always something that we have to pay close attention to."

Ana's story also gave the team an opportunity to seed characters that hadn't yet been released. One example is Sojourn, who is featured in the photograph. The team had already created concept art for the character, and they were planning to introduce her into the game at some point in the future. Although that day wouldn't come until a few years later—Sojourn was announced as a playable character for *Overwatch 2* at BlizzCon in 2019—the developers wanted to hint at her importance early on. ▼

DEPICTING VIOLENCE

▲ A crucial moment in Ana's origin piece is her encounter with the sniper Widowmaker—a meeting that ends with Ana losing an eye and, ultimately, being forced to go into hiding. The original image of this event showed Ana crumpled on the ground, blood pooling around her head, which raised questions about how to depict violence in Overwatch. The game is centered around player-versus-player combat, but it doesn't feature blood or gore. Should this approach to depicting violence hold true for the cinematics as well?

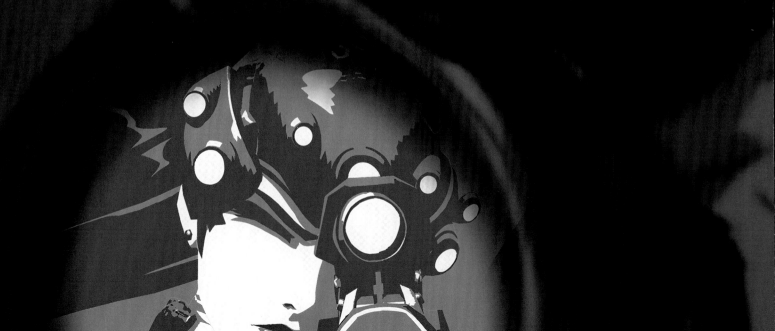

OPPOSITE, TOP Early illustration of Ana teaching Pharah how to use a sniper rifle, which was later replaced with an image of the mother teaching her daughter tae kwon do.

BELOW Sketch of Ana and Widowmaker facing off.

RIGHT Sketches of Ana after she was shot by Widowmaker. The amount of blood was reduced in the final images.

FOLLOWING PAGES The final image of Ana from her origin story.

The team decided it should. Creating visual and thematic cohesion between Overwatch's different media had been a goal from the beginning. The illustration of Ana was revised to reduce the amount of blood, leaving only a few streaks on the floor to show she had been wounded.

Questions about violence also prompted changes to another illustration in the origin story. In the final version of the piece, Ana practices tae kwon do with Pharah. An earlier version of the image had the mother showing her daughter how to use a sniper rifle. Although the art itself wasn't violent, the act of teaching a child how to use a gun didn't feel appropriate for Overwatch, a world built on themes of hope and a better future. ▼

SOMBRA

"THE CHALLENGE IS EVERY STORY IS DIFFERENT, SO WE CAN'T DO THE SAME STUFF AS WE DID BEFORE. WE'RE TRYING TO MAKE A NEW SONG."

—MIKE KOIZUMI, LEAD STORYBOARD ARTIST

SOMBRA'S ORIGIN WAS DIFFERENT FROM ITS PREDECESSORS in many ways. It was the first origin story directly tied to an animated short; it premiered at BlizzCon on November 4, 2016, on the heels of the "Infiltration" cinematic. It also pushed the boundaries of the origin story format by featuring traditional 2D animation instead of still images with effects and subtle movements added.

This approach sprang from the team's willingness to evolve the origin stories' format, beginning with "A Moment in Crime Special Report: 'The Junkers,'" which had added full color. "The Junkers' origin piece made us realize that we should continue to try to experiment with presenting the stories using new structures," said *Overwatch*'s former lead writer Michael Chu, who wrote the Sombra piece.

Sombra's origin touches on different periods of her life, from her days as a young hacker in the Los Muertos gang to her current quest to uncover the truth behind the shadowy power brokers who control the world.

The process of creating the story began much like it had with previous pieces. The team brainstormed ideas for images and dialogue, which were then combined into a rough animatic. But to bring the origin story to life in 2D animation, they also reached out to storyboard and visual development artists Craig Harris, Justin Thavirat, Vasili Zorin, and Mio Del Rosario.

"We were a little bold with this one," said lead character artist Arnold Tsang, who helped create art for the piece and guide the creative vision. "We wanted to see if we could change the aesthetic a little bit too. We tried to do a 2D anime style. It felt like the right hero to do it with."

RIGHT In-progress illustration of a young Sombra receiving cybernetic upgrades.

TRANSFORMING THE CHARACTER

▲ Bringing Sombra into the world of 2D animation required reimagining her appearance. To do so, the team created a character sheet for her, defining a look that the artists on the project could follow as production moved forward.

Compared to Sombra's original concept art, the 2D animation version of her features fewer layers of clothing and simpler textures, colors, and lighting effects. The goal with these adjustments was to preserve Sombra's iconic features while expressing them in a new way that fit the 2D aesthetic and made her easier to animate. ▼

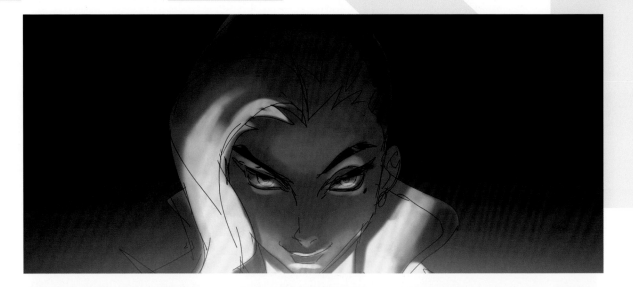

ABOVE Young Sombra created for 2D animation.

RIGHT In-progress illustrations for the origin piece.

OPPOSITE, TOP Line art for a sequence at the beginning of the piece.

OPPOSITE, BOTTOM Design for the web of information that Sombra displays at the end of the piece.

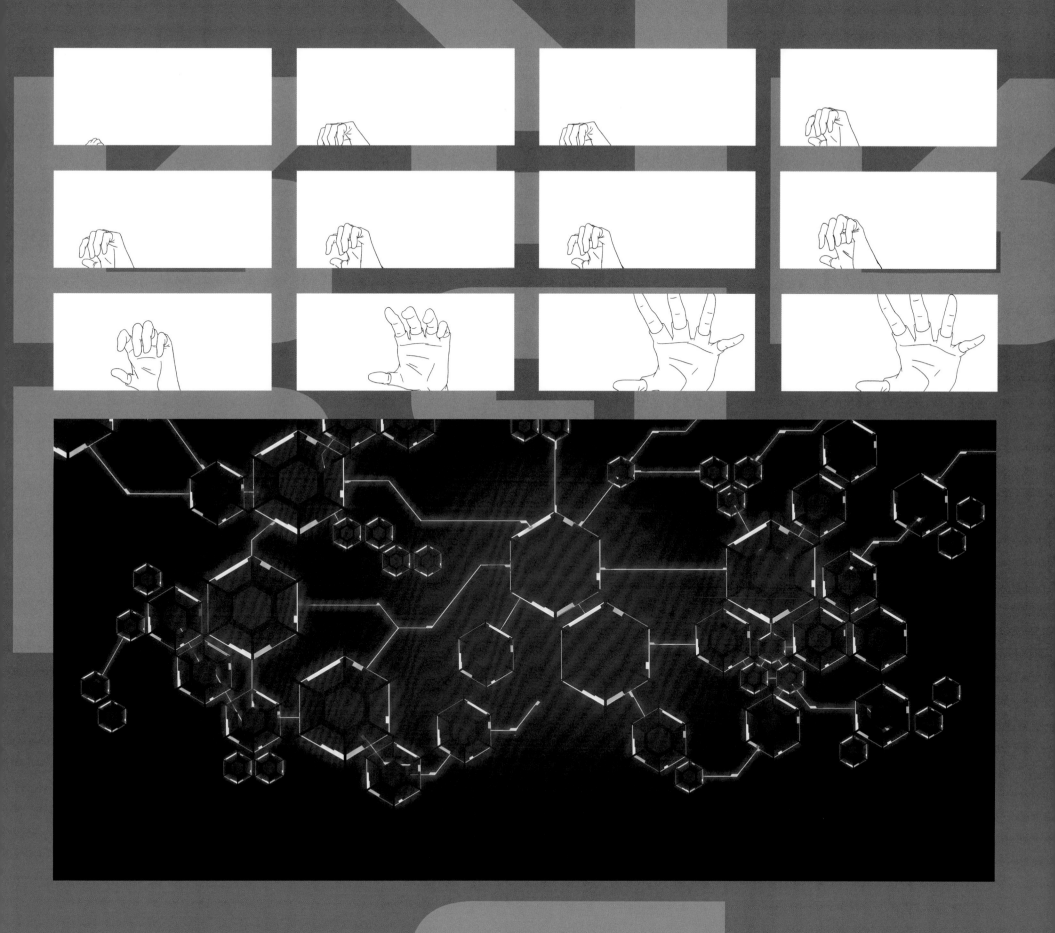

THESE PAGES In-progress illustrations of young Sombra interacting with the Los Muertos gang.

FOLLOWING PAGES Final illustration of Sombra receiving cybernetic upgrades.

CONCLUSION

FOUR
▼

BY THE RELEASE OF "INFILTRATION" AND SOMBRA'S ORIGIN STORY, THREE YEARS HAD PASSED SINCE THAT SUMMER DAY IN 2013 WHEN BLIZZARD Entertainment had taken its first step into the unknown. The team had released nine 3D-animated films and five 2D origin stories for Overwatch, totaling over sixty minutes of footage.

To complete these projects, they had evolved their art style, adopted new technologies, and developed a culture of collaboration. With each film, they had also made new discoveries about what the world of Overwatch was and how they could bring it to life through cinematics.

But even three years on, the journey was still young. There were many more Overwatch characters to introduce, many more artistic styles yet to explore, and many more stories yet to tell ...

THIS PAGE Render of Widowmaker.

DEDICATION

FOR

YVAIN GNABRO

CINEMATIC ANIMATOR (2015-2016)

During production of "The Last Bastion," one of the talented animators who worked on the film, Yvain Gnabro, passed away. The team decided to dedicate that cinematic to him—and mirrors that act here by dedicating this book to his memory. Yvain's passion for art and animation will live forever through the characters he brought to life. His constant pursuit of becoming a better artist and his unshakable joy for life will be remembered by all who knew him.

THIS PAGE Shots from "The Last Bastion" and "Alive" that Yvain worked on.

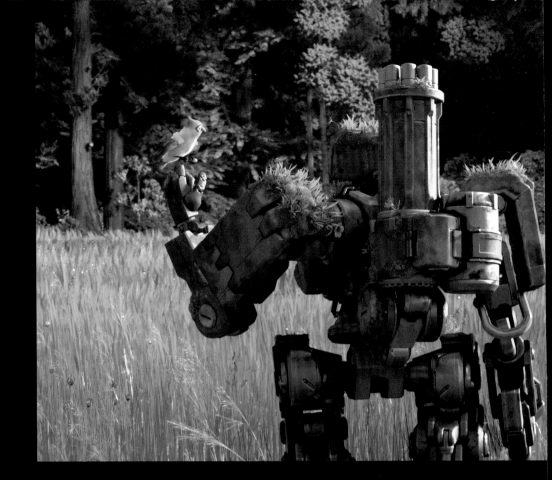

THE HEROES OF THE OVERWATCH UNIVERSE
ARE A DIVERSE GROUP OF PEOPLE WHO COME
TOGETHER TO BUILD A BETTER FUTURE.

THE SAME IS TRUE OF THE TALENTED
PROFESSIONALS WHO HAVE POURED THEIR
LOVE AND PASSION INTO DEVELOPING
THE GAME AND ITS CINEMATICS. THANK
YOU FOR EVERYTHING YOU HAVE DONE
TO BUILD AND SUPPORT SOMETHING
AS ASPIRATIONAL AS OVERWATCH.

TO THE REST OF THE BLIZZARD FAMILY:
GAMES LIKE THIS, CINEMATICS LIKE THIS,
AND BOOKS LIKE THIS SIMPLY WOULDN'T
EXIST WITHOUT YOUR WORK.

TO THE MILLIONS OF PLAYERS AROUND
THE WORLD WHO HAVE MADE A HOME IN
OVERWATCH AND BROUGHT IT TO LIFE
THROUGH ART, COSPLAY, AND OTHER WAYS:
THANK YOU FOR DARING TO SEE THE WORLD
FOR WHAT IT COULD BE, ALONG WITH US.

WRITTEN BY MATT BURNS

LEAD EDITOR JAKE GERLI

ART DIRECTION CHRIS THUNIG

LORE CONSULTATION MADI BUCKINGHAM,
SEAN COPELAND, JUSTIN PARKER, ANNE STICKNEY

PRODUCTION CHLOE FRABONI, BRIANNE MESSINA,
PAUL MORRISSEY, DEREK ROSENBERG,
DAVID SEEHOLZER, ANNA WAN

DIRECTOR, CONSUMER PRODUCTS
BYRON PARNELL

SPECIAL THANKS
LAUREL AUSTIN, STEPHAN BELIN, TED BOONTHANAKIT, DENNIS BREDOW,
JEFF CHAMBERLAIN, STEVEN CHEN, MICHAEL CHU, SHIMON COHEN,
KEVIN CROOK, BEN DAI, HUNTER GRANT, DOUG GREGORY, TERRAN GREGORY, JASON HILL,
PHILIP HILLENBRAND, KIM-SEANG HONG, MONIQUE JACQUES, JERAMIAH JOHNSON, JEFF
KAPLAN, ROMAN KENNEY, CLAVER KNOVICK, MIKE KOIZUMI, GEORGE KRSTIC, JUNGAH LEE,
TIMOTHY LOUGHRAN, CHRIS METZEN, WILL MURAI, YEWON PARK, KAITLIN PETERSON, BILL
PETRAS, JUSTIN RASCH, JACOB RIVERA, ANDREW ROBINSON, DAVID SATCHWELL, NATHAN
SCHAUF, JUSTIN THAVIRAT, ARNOLD TSANG, KEVIN VANDERJAGT, MATHIAS VERHASSELT,
MEG VOLLMER, JAMES WAUGH, JULIA ZSOLNAY

TITAN BOOKS

A division of Titan Publishing Group Ltd

144 Southwark Street. London SE1 0UP

www.titanbooks.com

Find us on Facebook: www.facebook.com/titanbooks

Follow us on Twitter: @TitanBooks

A CIP catalogue record for this title is available
from the British Library.

ISBN: 9781789095715

Printed in China

BOOK DESIGN BY **CAMERON + COMPANY**
PUBLISHER CHRIS GRUENER
CREATIVE DIRECTOR IAIN R. MORRIS
DESIGNER ROB DOLGAARD

PAGE 1 Illustration for the statue of
Jack Morrison, which appeared in the
announcement trailer.

PAGES 2-3 Final render of Reaper.

PAGE 4 Concept art of Volskaya Industries,
made for the "Infiltration" animated short.

PAGES 6-7 Illustration depicting Jack Morrison
from the announcement trailer.

THIS PAGE Illustration of a member of Overwatch
from the announcement trailer.

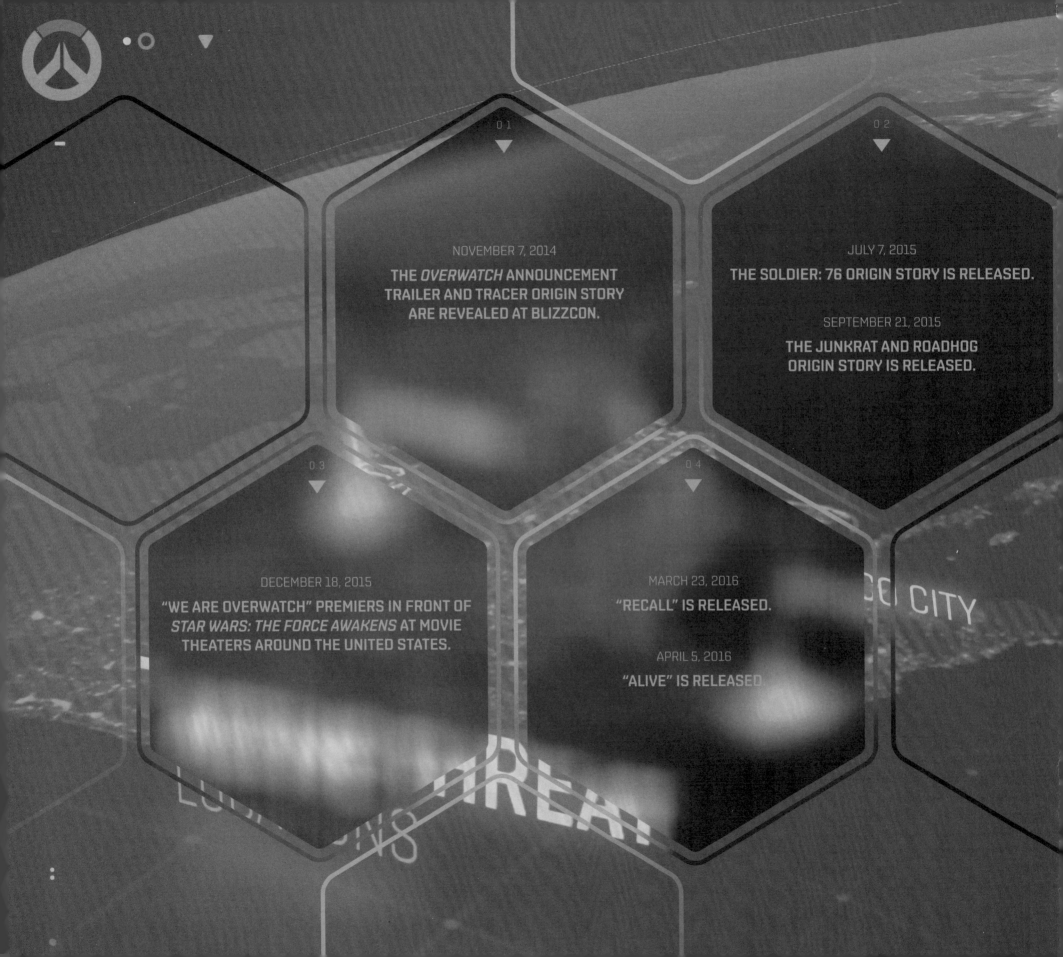

NOVEMBER 7, 2014

THE *OVERWATCH* ANNOUNCEMENT
TRAILER AND TRACER ORIGIN STORY
ARE REVEALED AT BLIZZCON.

JULY 7, 2015

THE SOLDIER: 76 ORIGIN STORY IS RELEASED.

SEPTEMBER 21, 2015

THE JUNKRAT AND ROADHOG
ORIGIN STORY IS RELEASED.

DECEMBER 18, 2015

"WE ARE OVERWATCH" PREMIERS IN FRONT OF
STAR WARS: THE FORCE AWAKENS AT MOVIE
THEATERS AROUND THE UNITED STATES.

MARCH 23, 2016

"RECALL" IS RELEASED.

APRIL 5, 2016

"ALIVE" IS RELEASED.